REVISE EDEXCEL GCSE (9–1)
Computer Science

REVISION WORKBOOK

Series Consultant: Harry Smith

Author: Navtej Marwaha

Also available to support your revision:

Revise GCSE Study Skills Guide   9781447967071

The **Revise GCSE Study Skills Guide** is full of tried-and-trusted hints and tips for how to learn more effectively. It gives you techniques to help you achieve your best – throughout your GCSE studies and beyond!

Revise GCSE Revision Planner   9781447967828

The **Revise GCSE Revision Planner** helps you to plan and organise your time, step-by-step, throughout your GCSE revision. Use this book and wall chart to mastermind your revision.

> **For the full range of Pearson revision titles across KS2, KS3, GCSE, Functional Skills, AS/A Level and BTEC visit:**
> www.pearsonschools.co.uk/revise

Contents

A small bit of small print

Edexcel publishes Sample Assessment Material and the Specification on its website. This is the official content and this book should be used in conjunction with it. The questions have been written to help you practise every topic in the book. Remember: the real exam questions may not look like this.

Algorithms

1 (a) What is an 'algorithm'?

....

.... **(1 mark)**

(b) The three programming constructs used in algorithms are sequence, selection and iteration.
The table below shows an algorithm for authenticating a user's login name and
password, which allows only three attempts.
Enter sequence, selection or iteration in the blank cell. **(5 marks)**

Line number	Instruction	Sequence, selection or iteration
1	If username is not recognised, inform the user that the username is not recognised	
2	Return to step 1	
3	If username is recognised, set number of attempts to 1	
4	Enter password	
5	If password does not match the stored password and the number of attempts is equal to 3, inform the user that the password is incorrect	
6	Increase number of attempts by 1	
7	Return to step 4	
8	If password does not match the stored password and the number of attempts is equal to 3, inform the user they have had three attempts	
9	Return to step 1	
10	If password does match the username, allow user into the system	

(c) An algorithm can be written and displayed as plain, written text.
State **two** other ways of displaying algorithms.

1 ....

....

2 ....

.... **(2 marks)**

Algorithms: pseudo-code

1   (a)   State what is meant by the term 'pseudo-code'.

....

....

....

.... **(2 marks)**

    (b)   Write an algorithm to convert an 8-bit binary number into a denary number. You can assume that the binary number is correctly formatted as 1s and 0s and has the correct number of digits so that validation is not required. Use pseudo-code.

> The algorithm should examine each of the 8 binary digits and multiply them by their place values. It should then find the total of these multiplications. See page 32 of the Revision Guide for a reminder on converting binary to denary.
>
> You will have a copy of the pseudo-code command set in the exam. Make sure your pseudo-code is clear, concise and accurate, and answers the question.

....

....

....

....

....

....

....

....

....

....

....

....

....

....

....

.... **(6 marks)**

Algorithms: flowcharts

1   The algorithm for a game simulates the throwing of three dice to find the player's score.
   • If all three are equal, then the score is the total of the dice.
   • If two are equal, the score is equal to the sum of the two equal dice minus the third.
   • If none are equal, then the score is zero.
   Here is part of a flowchart for the algorithm.

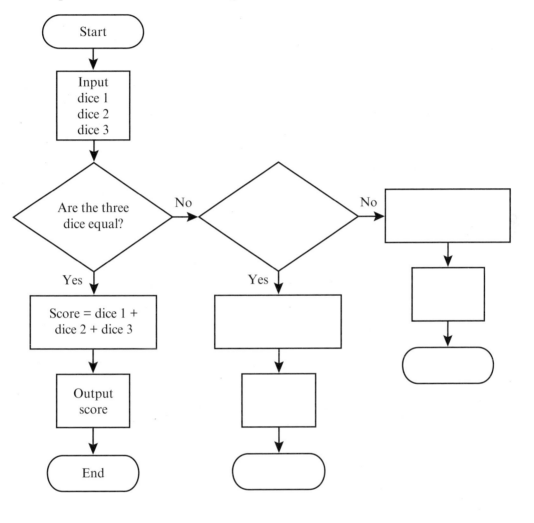

   (a)   Complete the flowchart for the algorithm.   **(6 marks)**

   (b)   Use the algorithm to calculate the score from the following dice throws.

       3 6 3

   ....

       5 4 5

   ....   **(2 marks)**

   (c)   It is possible to obtain a negative score using the algorithm.
         State **three** dice numbers which would result in a negative score.

   ....   **(1 mark)**

Purpose of an algorithm

1 Examine the following algorithm. In this algorithm, 'names' is an array.

```
SEND 'Please enter the first name.' TO DISPLAY
RECEIVE firstName FROM (STRING) KEYBOARD
SEND 'Please enter the family name.' TO DISPLAY
RECEIVE familyName = FROM (STRING) KEYBOARD
SEND 'Please enter the last two digits of the intake year.' TO DISPLAY
RECEIVE intYear FROM (INTEGER) KEYBOARD
SEND 'Please enter tutor group.' TO DISPLAY
RECEIVE tutorGroup FROM (STRING) KEYBOARD
SET index TO 1
SET unique TO false
WHILE unique = false DO
    loginName = intYear & familyName & firstName(0) & tutorGroup & index
    FOR check FROM 0 TO LENGTH(names) - 1 DO
        IF names[check] = loginName THEN
            SET index TO index + 1
        ELSE
            SET unique TO true
        END IF
    END FOR
END WHILE
SEND loginName TO DISPLAY
```

 (a) State the purpose of this algorithm.

....

.... **(2 marks)**

(b) State the inputs required by the algorithm.

....

.... **(4 marks)**

 (c) An array named 'names' is used in the algorithm. State the role of the variable named 'check'.

....

.... **(1 mark)**

 (d) State the login name for the following: Rosie Cooper in the intake year of 2001 and in tutor group Red. Assume that her login name is unique.

.... **(5 marks)**

(e) State **four** facts that you can deduce about the following student: 02GranthamOBlue3.

....

....

....

.... **(4 marks)**

Completing algorithms

1 Complete the following algorithm which is designed to find the largest of three numbers.

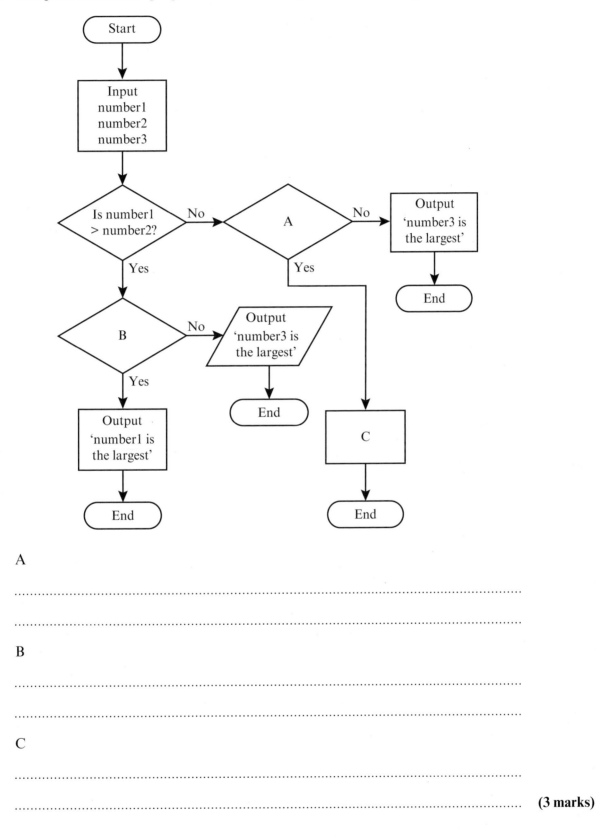

A

....

....

B

....

....

C

....

.... **(3 marks)**

Interpreting correct output

1 Rosie is writing an algorithm to work out the change to be given to a customer in a car park payment system.
This flowchart is incomplete and does not show all the possible combinations of notes and coins.

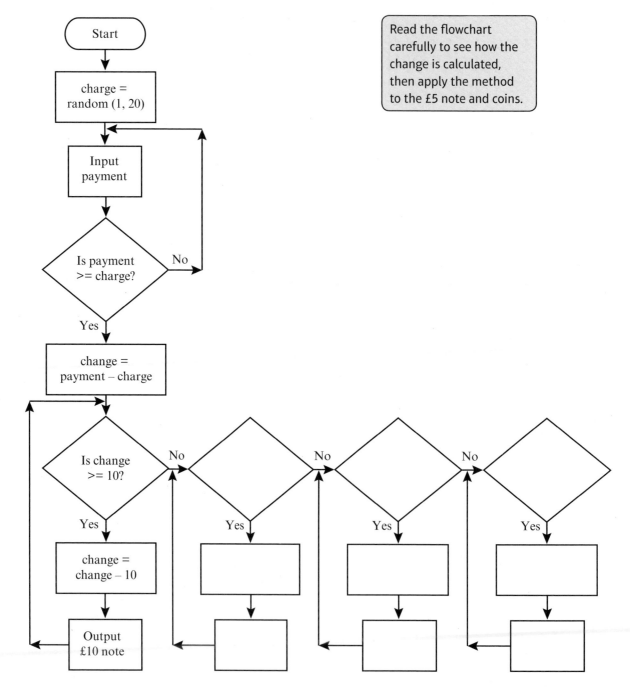

> Read the flowchart carefully to see how the change is calculated, then apply the method to the £5 note and coins.

Complete the flowchart to show how the numbers of £5 notes and £2 and £1 coins in the change will be calculated. Write your answer in the empty symbols. **(9 marks)**

Using trace tables

1 Here is an algorithm expressed in pseudo-code.

```
1    SET list TO [5, 9, 2, 5, 13]
2    RECEIVE item FROM (INTEGER) KEYBOARD
3    SET found TO false
4    FOR search FROM 0 to LENGTH(list) DO
5        IF item = list[search] THEN
6            found = true
7        END IF
8    END FOR
9    IF found = true THEN
10   SEND 'The item is in the list.' TO DISPLAY
11   ELSE
12   SEND 'The item is not in the list.' TO DISPLAY
13   END IF
```

> Before you start, read through the algorithm very carefully. Make sure that you understand what the algorithm is intended to do. That will help you to find the error in the pseudo-code in part (b).

(a) Identify the data structure used to store the numbers in the list.

.... **(1 mark)**

(b) There is an error in the pseudo-code.

  (i) State the number of the line in which there is an error.

.... **(1 mark)**

  (ii) Give the correct version of this pseudo-code.

.... **(1 mark)**

(c) Complete the trace table to show the execution of the algorithm if the search item is 13. You may not need to fill in all the rows in the table.

item	found	search	list[search]	output

(5 marks)

Identifying and correcting errors

1 Part of an algorithm that a student has created to simulate the change given by a payment system is shown below. A user enters their payment and the algorithm determines the notes and coins that should be returned.

```
1    SET charge to RANDOM(0, 50)
2    SET payment TO 0
3    SET money TO 0
4    SEND 'Please enter payment' TO DISPLAY
4    RECEIVE money FROM (REAL)KEYBOARD
6    SET payment TO payment + money
7    WHILE payment < charge DO
8        SEND 'The charge is ' & charge & '. Please enter more money.' TO DISPLAY
9        RECEIVE money FROM (REAL) keyboard
10       SET payment TO payment - money
11   END WHILE
12       SET change TO payment - charge
13       SEND 'Thank you. Change required is £ & change TO DISPLAY
14   WHILE change >= 10.00 DO
15       SEND '£10 note' TO DISPLAY
16       SET change TO change - 10.00
17   END WHILE
18   WHILE change > 5 DO
19       SEND '£5 note' TO DISPLAY
20       SET change TO change - 5.00
21   END WHILE
22   WHILE change >= 2.00 DO
23       SEND '£2 coin' TO DISPLAY
24       SET change TO change + 2.00
25   END WHILE
```

There are **five** errors in this algorithm. Some are logic errors and some are syntax errors. Identify the line numbers and correct the errors.

1 ....

2 ....

3 ....

4 ....

5 .... **(5 marks)**

Linear search

1 (a) Describe how a linear search algorithm works.

....

....

....

....   **(2 marks)**

(b) David has compiled a list of all the people invited to his party and has stored the names in an array called partyList.
Write an algorithm in pseudo-code to check whether Elaine's name is on the list. Use pseudo-code.

> The answer should, if possible, be written in the Edexcel pseudo-code, but you may use any style of pseudo-code providing its meaning can be understood by a competent programmer.

....

....

....

....

....

....

....

....

....

....

....

....

....

....

....

....

....

....   **(6 marks)**

Binary search

1   Describe the stages of a binary search on a list of items sorted in ascending order.

....

....

....

....

....

....

.... **(4 marks)**

2   A student has the following list of friends.

Ahmed	Ann	Claire	David	Mary	Matt	Peter	Stephen	Zoe

Show the stages of a binary search
to find the name 'Stephen' from the
data shown in the list.

> You should indicate which item will be selected
> each time and then show the new sub-list.

....

....

....

....

....

.... **(4 marks)**

3   Show the stages of a binary search to find the number '9' from the data shown in
this table.

1	6	9	13	15	21	28	36	42	69	76	85	94

....

....

....

....

....

.... **(4 marks)**

Comparing linear and binary searches

1   Complete the flowchart of a binary search by labelling the empty symbols.   **(5 marks)**

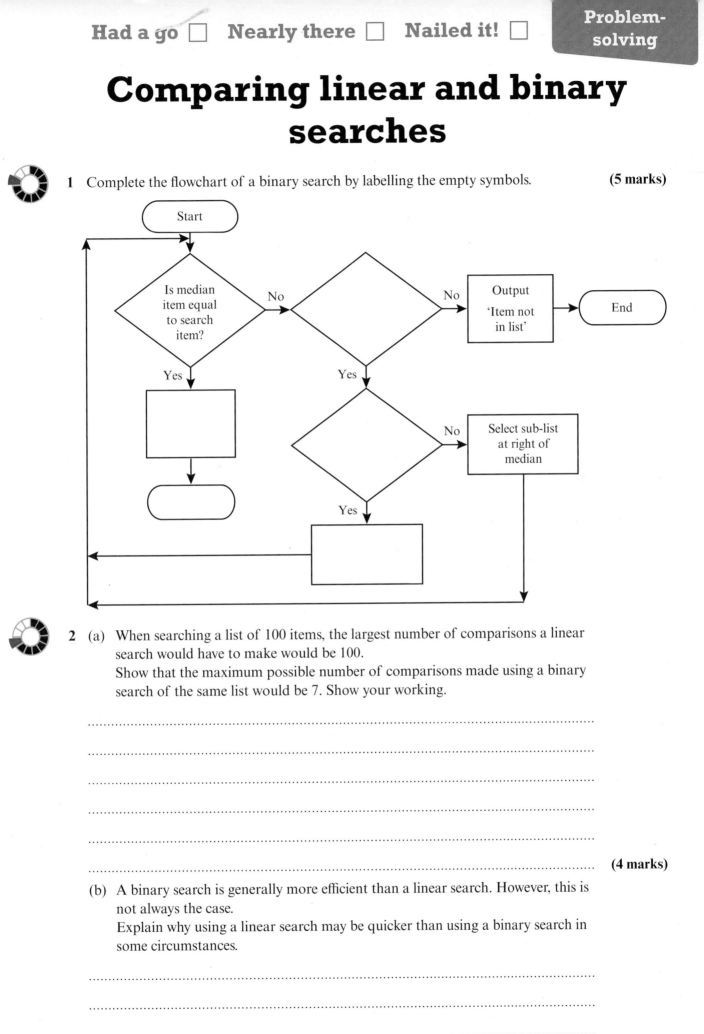

2   (a)   When searching a list of 100 items, the largest number of comparisons a linear
search would have to make would be 100.
Show that the maximum possible number of comparisons made using a binary
search of the same list would be 7. Show your working.

....

....

....

....

....

....   **(4 marks)**

   (b)   A binary search is generally more efficient than a linear search. However, this is
not always the case.
Explain why using a linear search may be quicker than using a binary search in
some circumstances.

....

....

....

....   **(2 marks)**

11

Bubble sort

1 This list of numbers must be sorted into ascending order.

| 20 | 15 | 3 | 13 | 9 | 2 | 6 |

Show the stages of a bubble sort when applied to the data shown in the list.

> You should label each pass and remember to compare each pair of numbers and switch them round if they are not in the correct order.

....

....

....

....

....

....   **(4 marks)**

2 The table below shows an algorithm for carrying out a bubble sort, but the lines are not in the correct order.
Complete the table to show the correct order of the lines.

Order	Line
1	`SET swapped to True`
	`END FOR`
	`FOR index FROM 1 to LENGTH(list) - 1 DO`
3	`SET swapped to False`
	`IF list[index - 1] > list[index] THEN`
	`SET swapped TO True`
10	`END IF`
6	`SET temp TO list[index] - 1`
	`WHILE swapped = True`
	`SET list[index - 1] TO list[index]`
	`END WHILE`
	`SET list[index] TO temp`

> A loop will need to be set up to move through the list to compare the adjacent values and swap them if they are in the wrong order. It will have to run until there are no swaps.
>
> The best responses should:
> - place the start and end of the while loop in the correct positions
> - order the lines of the swap correctly
> - put the start and end of the if statements in the correct positions
> - set the value of the swapped variable correctly.

(5 marks)

Merge sort

1   The merge sort algorithm divides up a list into smaller and smaller sections and then sorts them into order before putting them back together again.
Explain the advantage of using this technique.

....

....

....

....   **(2 marks)**

2   Use a merge sort to put the data shown below into ascending order.
Show all the stages of the process.

33	25	46	2	8	69	9

....

....

....

....

....

....

....

....

....

....

....

....

....

....   **(6 marks)**

Decomposition and abstraction

1   Danika is creating a computer version of the game 'rock-paper-scissors'. The rules for winning are shown in the figure.

- Rock 'blunts' scissors. Rock wins.
- Scissors 'cut' the paper. Scissors win.
- Paper 'covers' the rock. Paper wins.

In Danika's game, the computer will take the place of one of the human players and will randomly generate a letter (R, S or P) to represent one of the objects.
She has created a subprogram named 'computerTurn' to generate the computer's letter.

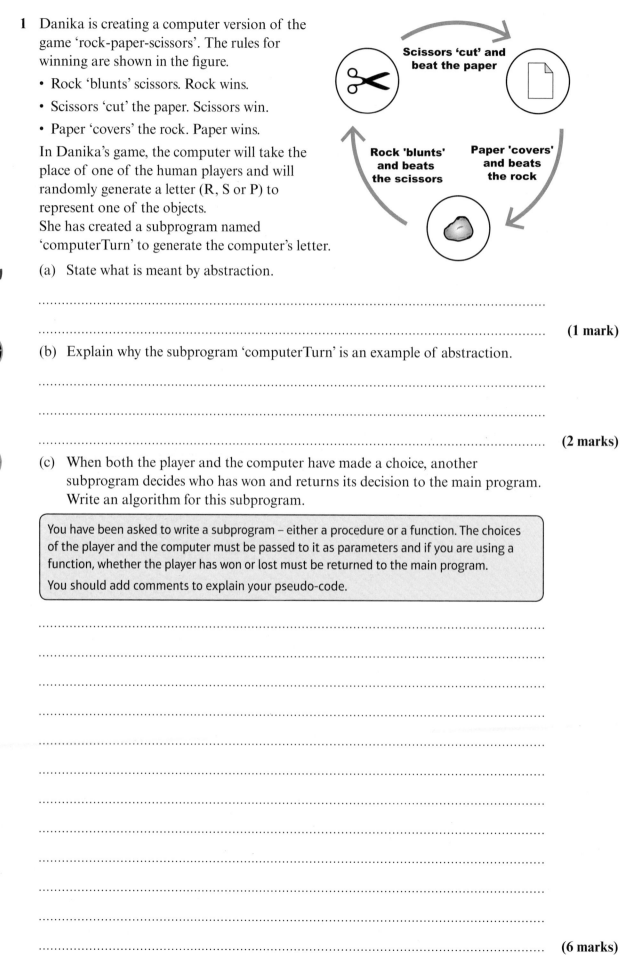

(a)   State what is meant by abstraction.

....

.... **(1 mark)**

(b)   Explain why the subprogram 'computerTurn' is an example of abstraction.

....

....

.... **(2 marks)**

(c)   When both the player and the computer have made a choice, another subprogram decides who has won and returns its decision to the main program. Write an algorithm for this subprogram.

> You have been asked to write a subprogram – either a procedure or a function. The choices of the player and the computer must be passed to it as parameters and if you are using a function, whether the player has won or lost must be returned to the main program.
>
> You should add comments to explain your pseudo-code.

....

....

....

....

....

....

....

....

....

....

.... **(6 marks)**

Variables and constants

1   Program code makes use of variables and constants.

(a)   Explain what is meant by a variable.

....

....   **(2 marks)**

(b)   State how a constant differs from a variable.

....

....   **(1 mark)**

(c)   State why variables and constants should be given meaningful names.

....

....   **(1 mark)**

(d)   The algorithm shown below searches for a value in a list.

```
1  SET mysteryNumber TO 6
2  SET correct TO False
3  WHILE correct = False DO
4      RECEIVE guess FROM (INTEGER) KEYBOARD
5      IF guess = mysteryNumber THEN
6          set correct to True
7      END IF
8  END WHILE
```

Complete the table to show the variables used and why they are used in the program.

> Read the algorithm carefully to identify the variables and to understand why they have been used. The first one has been done for you.

Guided

Variable	Use within the program
mysteryNumber	This is used to hold the number which must be guessed.

(6 marks)

Arithmetic operators

1 Calculate the result of the following expression using the correct order of operations. Show the result of each stage.
The first one has been done for you.

result = 6 * 8 / 2 + (15 − 6) + 3^3

result = 6 * 8 / 2 + 9 + 3^3

....

....

....

.... **(4 marks)**

2 Complete the table below by filling in the value of number after each line of code is executed. The first one has been done for you.

Code	Resultnumber
number = 12 + 6 / 2	number = 15
number = 6 * 3 / 2	
number = 23 MOD 6	
number = 23 DIV 6	
number = 6 ^ 2	

(4 marks)

3 A number trick asks you to think of a number, double it, add six, divide it in half and then subtract the number you started with. The result should always be 3.
Write an algorithm using pseudo-code that asks a user to input a number, then carries out each of the operations and outputs the result.

> Read the question very carefully to identify all the arithmetic operations needed. You should see that you will need two variables to store the numbers!
>
> Do a dry run of your algorithm to check that the result is correct.

....

....

....

....

....

....

....

....

....

.... **(3 marks)**

Relational operators

1 Complete the table below by evaluating each of the statements listed and stating whether it is True or False.

The first one has been done for you.

Statement	True/False
7 * 3 <> 10 + 11	False
8 + 10 > 8 * 2	
9 * 3 <= 10 + 17	
10 + 15 >= 6 * 5	
9 * 2 = 6 * 3	

> You first need to work out the results of the calculations and then compare them using the operators.

(5 marks)

2 Alina has sto1red her computer science marks in an array named 'marks'.

Write an algorithm using pseudo-code that prompts Alina to enter a new mark and then outputs the number of marks in the array that are:

equal to it

less than it

greater than it.

....

....

....

....

....

....

....

....

....

....

....

....

....

....

....

....

.... **(6 marks)**

Logical operators

1 Complete the table below to show the output of each algorithm.
The first solution has been completed for you.

> Read and work through the algorithms carefully and write the expected outcome in the second column.

⟩ Guided ⟩

Algorithm	Output

SET number TO 3
IF number > 0 AND number < 2 THEN
   SEND 'Within range.' TO DISPLAY
ELSE
   SEND 'Out of range.' TO DISPLAY
END IF
	Out of range.

SET number TO 6
IF NOT(number = 3) OR number <> 5 THEN
   SEND 'Number is acceptable.' TO DISPLAY
ELSE
   SEND 'Number is not acceptable.' TO DISPLAY
END IF	

SET colour TO 'red'
SET size TO 'm'
SET price to 25
IF colour = 'blue' OR colour = 'red' AND size = 'm'
AND price <= 30 THEN
   SEND 'This would be OK.' TO DISPLAY
ELSE
   SEND 'Not OK.' TO DISPLAY
END IF	

SET number1 TO 6
SET number2 TO 9
IF (number1 <= 9 OR number2 >=10) AND NOT(number1 *
number2 <50) AND (number2 – number1 = 3) THEN
   SEND 'These numbers are OK.' TO DISPLAY
ELSE
   SEND 'Not OK.' TO DISPLAY
END IF	

(3 marks)

Selection

1 A teacher wants a program that will output a comment when a mark is input, according to the following rules.

Mark	Comment
90 and above	Excellent
70 to 89	Very good
60 to 69	Good
50 to 59	Satisfactory
Below 50	Unsatisfactory

> The algorithm should allow the teacher to enter a mark and then use comparison operators to decide the range the mark is in and display the appropriate comment.
>
> Be careful when you are selecting the ranges. A mark can only be put in one range.

Write an algorithm using pseudo-code that prompts the teacher to enter a mark and then displays the appropriate comment.

....

....

....

....

....

....

....

....

....

....

....

....

....

....

....

....

....

....

....

.... **(5 marks)**

Iteration

1 The algorithm shown below searches for a value in a list.

```
SET list TO [5, 9, 2, 5, 13]
SEND 'Please enter the search item.' TO DISPLAY
RECEIVE item FROM (INTEGER) KEYBOARD
SET found TO False
FOR search FROM 0 TO LENGTH(list) -1 DO
   IF item = list[search] THEN
      SET found TO True
   END IF
END FOR
IF found = True THEN
   SEND 'The item is in the list.' TO DISPLAY
ELSE
   SEND 'The item is not in the list.' TO DISPLAY
END IF
```

The algorithm is not very efficient because it continues iterating through the list even if the search item has been found.
Rewrite the algorithm to improve the efficiency by stopping the search when the item has been found.

> You need to change the algorithm so that it breaks out of the loop if the item is found.
>
> Remember – there is another type of loop!

....

....

....

....

....

....

....

....

....

....

....

....

....

.... **(4 marks)**

Data types

1 The following algorithm allows a user to enter data about themselves and the number of whole hours they worked each day for a week.

```
SEND 'Please enter your name.' TO DISPLAY
RECEIVE name FROM (STRING) KEYBOARD
SEND 'Please enter your gender as 'F' or 'M'.' TO DISPLAY
RECEIVE gender FROM (CHARACTER) KEYBOARD
SEND 'Enter the number of days you worked this week.' TO DISPLAY
RECEIVE daysWorked FROM (INTEGER) KEYBOARD
IF daysWorked = 5 THEN
   SET fullWeek TO True
END IF
IF fullWeek = True THEN
   SET hoursWorked TO 0
   FOR day FROM 1 to 5 DO
      SEND 'Please enter complete hours worked for day.' & day & '.' TO DISPLAY
      RECEIVE oneDay FROM KEYBOARD
      SET hoursWorked TO hoursWorked + oneDay
   END FOR
   SET meanHoursWorked TO hoursWorked / 5
   SEND 'Mean hours worked per day this week = ' & meanHoursWorked TO DISPLAY
ELSE
   SEND 'Five day week not worked.' TO DISPLAY
END IF
```

(a) Complete the table below by giving an example of a variable used in the algorithm above for each of the data types listed. One has been done for you.

Guided

Data type	Variable
Real	meanHoursWorked
Boolean	
Integer	
Character	

(4 marks)

(b) The algorithm is to be extended to calculate the user's weekly pay.
State **two** additional variables that will be needed and identify the data type of each.

Variable 1

....

Data type

....

Variable 2

....

Data type

.... **(4 marks)**

String manipulation

1 The following algorithm is designed to manipulate a string.

```
SET subject TO 'Computer Science'
FOR index = 0 TO LENGTH(subject) - 1
  IF subject(index) = ' ' THEN
     SET position TO index
  END IF
NEXT FOR
SEND position TO DISPLAY
```

Complete the table below by stating the values of the variables listed.

Variable	Value
LENGTH(subject)	
position	

(2 marks)

2 Write an algorithm using pseudo-code that will analyse a sentence entered by a user and output the number of times each vowel occurs in the sentence.

> You need to find the length of the string so that the algorithm can traverse it to find the vowels.
>
> Remember that vowels are the letters a, e, i, o and u. The algorithm must be able to count upper and lower case letters as the same vowel.

....

....

....

....

....

....

....

....

....

....

....

....

.... **(5 marks)**

Arrays

1 (a) Describe what is meant by an array.

....

....

....

.... **(2 marks)**

Jack has taken his temperature every day for a week and has stored the readings in an array named 'temp'.

The data for the week has already been entered and stored in 'temp'.

(b) Write an algorithm using pseudo-code to display the minimum and maximum temperatures stored in the array.

....

....

....

....

....

....

....

....

....

....

.... **(4 marks)**

2 The figure shows a black and white bitmap image.
The image can be encoded using 1 to represent black pixels and 0 to represent white pixels.
Complete the matrix below to show how the pixel data could be stored in a two-dimensional array.
The first row has been done for you.

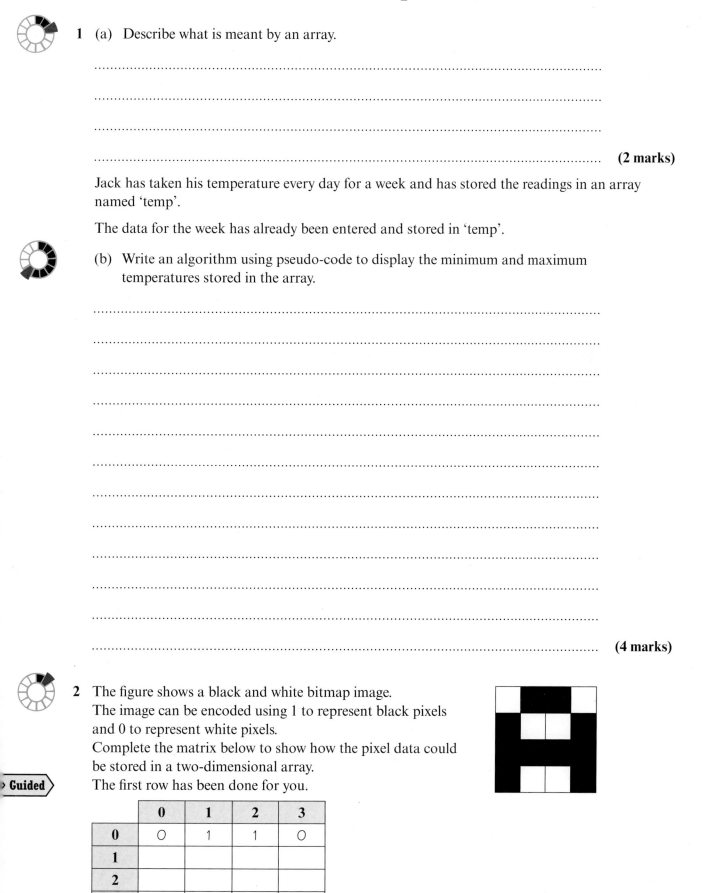

	0	1	2	3
0	O	1	1	O
1				
2				
3				

(3 marks)

File handling operations

1   The figure shows a black and white bitmap image.
This image can be encoded into a string named 'pixels' using
1 to represent black and 0 to represent white pixels.

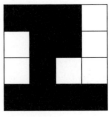

(a)   Write an algorithm using pseudo-code to store the pixel
data in a text file named 'shape.txt'.

....

....

....

....

....

....

....   **(4 marks)**

(b)   Write an algorithm using pseudo-code that would read the data from the file
'shape.txt' into a two-dimensional array named 'matrix'.

> Even if you aren't sure if you can answer the whole question, there may be parts you do
> know. For example, if you can't write the whole algorithm, you may pick up marks for
> opening and closing files correctly.

....

....

....

....

....

....

....

....

....

....

....

....   **(6 marks)**

Records

1 (a) Both records and arrays are data structures.

State **one** similarity and **one** difference between arrays and records.

Similarity ....

....

Difference ....

.... **(2 marks)**

(b) Dorothy Jackson is opening a cattery to look after animals when their owners go on holiday.

She wants to store information about the cats in a suitable data structure. The data is shown in the table below.

Name	Gender	Weight (kg)	Number of days	Special diet?
Dottie	F	3.2	6	N
Jack	M	4.2	7	Y
Tom	M	5.1	4	N

(i) Explain why records would be a more suitable data structure for storing this data than arrays.

....

....

....

.... **(2 marks)**

(ii) Explain how this data could be stored in a two-dimensional array.

....

....

....

.... **(2 marks)**

(iii) Explain how this data could be stored using one-dimensional arrays.

....

....

....

.... **(4 marks)**

Subprograms 1

1 When writing programs, computer scientists make use of subprograms.

(a) Explain what is meant by a subprogram.

....

....

....

.... **(2 marks)**

(b) Describe **two** advantages to a programmer of using subprograms.

1 ....

....

....

....

2 ....

....

....

.... **(4 marks)**

(c) Two types of subprogram are functions and procedures.
State **one** difference between these types of subprogram.

....

....

....

.... **(1 mark)**

2 This is a function to convert centimetres to inches.

```
1 FUNCTION centimetresToInches(measurement)
2 BEGIN FUNCTION
3   newMeasurement = measurement/2.54
4
5 END FUNCTION
```

(a) State the name of one parameter used in the function.

.... **(1 mark)**

(b) State **one** local variable used in the function.

.... **(1 mark)**

(c) Line 4 is missing. Complete line 4.

....

.... **(2 marks)**

Subprograms 2

1 The algorithm below uses a subprogram to find the area and circumference of rectangles.

```
1   FUNCTION calculate(length, width)
2   BEGIN FUNCTION
3       SET area TO length * width
4       SET circumference TO 2*length + 2*width
5       RETURN area, circumference
6   END function
7 #This is the main program
8 RECEIVE recLength FROM (REAL)KEYBOARD
9 RECEIVE recWidth FROM (REAL)KEYBOARD
10
11 SEND recArea & recCircumference TO DISPLAY
```

(a) Identify **two** global variables used in the algorithm.

1 ....

2 .... **(2 marks)**

(b) Identify **two** parameters used in the algorithm.

1 ....

2 .... **(2 marks)**

(c) Identify **two** local variables used in the algorithm.

1 ....

2 .... **(2 marks)**

(d) Line 10 is missing.
Complete line 10 to call the function.

.... **(2 marks)**

2 Write an algorithm using pseudo-code that uses a function to find the larger of any two different numbers entered by a user.

....

....

....

....

....

....

....

....

.... **(6 marks)**

27

Validation

1   Advika has decided to incorporate user authentication into her program. Users must register a username and password. A password must have at least eight characters, at least one of which must be an upper case letter.
Use pseudo-code to write a suitable password creation algorithm for Advika's program. The algorithm should include validation to check that a password has been entered, a check on the password requirements and suitable error messages.

....

....

....

....

....

....

....

....

....

....

....

....

....

....

....

....

....

....

....

....

....

....

(8 marks)

Testing and test plans

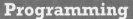

1 Mr Smart has written a program so that he can input the students' exam percentages into an array named 'marks' in the same order as the students' names stored in an array named 'students' that already contains their surnames. The program should also output the name of the student with the highest percentage.

```
1 SET maximum TO 0
2 FOR index FROM 0 TO LENGTH(students)
3    SEND 'Please enter the percentage mark for' & students[index] TO DISPLAY
4    RECEIVE percentage FROM (INTEGER) KEYBOARD
5    WHILE percentage > 100 OR percentage < 0 THEN
6    SEND 'Percentage must be 100 or less. Please enter the percentage mark for' +
students[index])
7        RECEIVE percentage FROM (INTEGER) KEYBOARD
8    END WHILE
9    SET marks[0] TO percentage
10   IF percentage < maximum THEN
11       SET maximum TO index
12   END IF
13 END FOR
14 SEND 'The student with the maximum mark is' & students[maximum]
```

Mr Smart has selected some data to test the program.

(a) Complete the table below to show the type of test and the expected result, based on the given test data.

> Look at page 29 of the Revision Guide to identify the type of test carried out in each case and then state the expected results. Will the data be accepted or not?

Test number	Type of test	Test data	Expected result
1		69	
2		99	
3		120	

(6 marks)

(b) There are **three** errors in Mr Smart's code.
Write down the line numbers and the correct versions of the code in the table below.

Line number	Correct version

(6 marks)

Using binary

1 Explain why all instructions and data used by a computer are represented in binary.

> You should explain the components used by the computer to carry out (execute) instructions and how they operate, the digits of the binary system and then how they relate to each other.

....

....

....

....

....

.... **(4 marks)**

2 If 4 binary digits are used to represent a colour in a graphics program, how many different colours can be represented?

☐ A 4
☐ B 8
☐ C 16
☐ D 32   **(1 mark)**

3 If 3 binary digits are used to represent a character, show the different combinations of digits that are possible.

> You should write down all of the unique combinations where each digit can be either a 0 or a 1.

000, 001, ...

.... **(3 marks)**

4 The denary value of each binary digit is given by its place value.
Complete the table below to show the denary value represented by each of the digits.

> The denary value is given by the binary digit multiplied by its place value.

1	0	1	1

(1 mark)

5 The same combination of digits can be used to represent many different items such as a program instruction, a character or a colour.
Explain how a computer interprets the combination as the correct item.

....

....

....

.... **(2 marks)**

Converting from denary to binary

1   Convert the denary number 199 into an 8-bit binary number.
    You must show your working.

> Remember to compare the denary number with the binary place value and calculate the remainder.
>
> You should always show your working in questions involving calculations. You may get some credit for showing that you understand the method even if the answer you come up with is wrong.

(2 marks)

2   Write an algorithm in pseudo-code to convert a whole denary number between 0 and 255 into an 8-bit binary number.

> You might want to use a data structure to store the place values that you are going to use and another one to store the digits of the binary number.

....

....

....

....

....

....

....

....

....

....

....

....

....

....

.... **(8 marks)**

Converting from binary to denary and binary addition

1   Convert the 8-bit binary number 10010111 into a denary number.
    You must show your working.

> Remember to multiply the binary digits by their place values. You could use a table to help you to do this.

10010111
128   16 421
   151

128
16
4
2
1
―――
151

(2 marks)

2   Add the following 8-bit binary numbers.
    Give your answer in 8-bit binary form.

0	1	0	1	0	1	1	1
0	1	0	1	1	1	1	1

1 1 1 1 0 1 1 0
1 1 1 1 1 1 1

(2 marks)

3   (a)   Add the following 8-bit binary numbers. Give your answer in 8-bit binary form.

1	1	0	0	1	0	1	1
1	0	0	1	0	1	1	1

0 1 1 0 0 0 1 0
1   1 1 1 1 1

(2 marks)

   (b)   (i)   Identify the problem that this addition has created.

   A over flow error   **(1 mark)**

   (ii) Explain why the error has occurred.

   Trying to carry the 1 to an
   empty collom

(2 marks)

4   A student was asked to add the 8-bit binary numbers, 01010111 and 01001010.
    Their answer was 10110001.

    Was their answer correct or incorrect? Show working to explain how you know.

   01010111   incorrect
   01001010   ✓
   10100001
   1 1 1 1 1 1

(3 marks)

Logical shifts

1 (a) Explain what is meant by a logical shift.

> You are being asked to 'explain', so you should give a detailed answer with at least two items of information.

....

....

....

.... **(2 marks)**

(b) Complete a 2 place logical shift left on the binary number 10101011.

.... **(2 marks)**

2 (a) State the effect of performing a 2 place logical shift right on a binary number.

....

.... **(1 mark)**

(b) Complete the following table to show the effect of performing a 2 place logical shift right on the binary number 10101101 and the denary equivalents of the number and the result.

> You must carry out the logical shift and also convert the numbers to decimal. This will help you to check that you have carried out the shift correctly.

Binary number	10101101	Decimal equivalent	
Binary number after a 2 place logical shift right		Decimal equivalent	

(3 marks)

(c) Explain the results shown in the table.

> You should state the divisor being used in a 2 place logical shift and any difference between the actual result and what would be expected if that divisor were used on the decimal number.

....

....

....

.... **(2 marks)**

Signed integers

1 (a) Explain how 'sign and magnitude' is used to indicate whether a binary number is positive or negative.

....

....

....

.... **(2 marks)**

(b) State **one** drawback of using this method.

....

.... **(1 mark)**

2 Complete the table to show the denary number 24 using 8-bit notation and the two's complement of that binary number.

24								
Two's complement								

(2 marks)

3 (a) Complete the table to calculate adding 30 in denary to –15 in denary using 8-bit notation and two's complement.

30								
–15								
Answer								

(3 marks)

(b) Complete the table to convert your answer to denary.

Answer								
Place values								

State the denary equivalent of your answer.

.... **(2 marks)**

4 Complete the table to calculate adding –10 in denary to –20 in denary using 8-bit notation and two's complement.

–10								
–20								
Answer								

(3 marks)

Arithmetic shifts

1   (a)   Describe the result of carrying out an arithmetic shift right to an 8-bit signed binary number.

> You are being asked to 'describe' and so you should give a detailed answer with at least two items of information in this case.

....

....

....

.... **(2 marks)**

(b)   Describe the result of carrying out an arithmetic shift left to an 8-bit signed binary number.

....

....

....

.... **(2 marks)**

2   Complete the table to show the effect of carrying out an arithmetic shift right, 3 places on the binary number 10010101 which is in two's complement format.

> Remember that this is an arithmetic shift on a signed number and not a logical shift.

Number	1	0	0	1	0	1	0	1
Result of shift								

(2 marks)

3   Complete the table to show the effect of carrying out an arithmetic shift left, 2 places on the binary number 10010101 which is in two's complement format.

Number	1	0	0	1	0	1	0	1
Result of shift								

(2 marks)

4   Complete the table to show the effect of multiplying denary −35 in two's complement format by 4.

35								
−35								
Result of multiplication								

(3 marks)

Hexadecimal and binary

1 (a) Explain why hexadecimal numbers are sometimes used to represent values stored in computers, even though computers do not use hexadecimal numbers.

Because it can represent every byte
as 2 digits not 8 lik binary.

(2 marks)

(b) Convert the hexadecimal number C3 into an 8-bit binary number.
You must show your working.

> Remember to first convert the two digits into denary numbers if they are letters. These can then be converted into the two nibbles of the binary number.

C3
12 3

12   3
11 00   00 11

C3 =   11 00 0011

(3 marks)

(c) Convert the 8-bit binary numbers 11010101 and 10111101 into hexadecimal numbers.
You must show your working.

> Remember to first convert the 8-bit number to nibbles and then convert each of these into a denary number.

(i) 11010101

D5

13=D   5
8 4 2 1   8 4 2 1
1 1 0 1   0 1 0 1

(2 marks)

(ii) 10111101

BD

11= B   13 = D
1 0 1 1   1 1 0 1
8 4 2 1   8 4 2 1

(2 marks)

Characters

1 (a) Explain what is meant by the character set of a computer.

....

....

.... **(2 marks)**

(b) Explain how ASCII is used to represent text in a computer system.

> You should say how many bits are used in the ASCII code and how many characters and actions can be represented.

....

....

....

....

....

.... **(3 marks)**

2 A student has written a function named ASC() that will take a character as a parameter and return the ASCII code in denary of that character.
Write a program using pseudo-code that will ask a user to enter a sentence and then output a string containing the ASCII codes.

....

....

....

....

....

....

....

....

....

....

....

....

....

....

.... **(6 marks)**

Bitmap images

1   Figure 1 is a bitmap image.

Figure 1

(a)   State what is meant by the following terms.

The size of an image

The ammount of storage taken up on a harddrive   It's width and height

The resolution of an image

It's size and clarity   its number of Pixels per inch

(2 marks)

(b)   The number of colours represented in an image depends on the colour depth used. Complete the table to show the number of colours that can be represented using the following colour depths.

Colour depth	Number of colours represented	
1	2	2^1
3	8	2^3
8	256	2^8

(3 marks)

(c)   The image in Figure 1 has the following properties: width = 2000; height = 3000; colour depth = 24.
Construct an expression to calculate the size of the image file in megabytes.

2000 × 3000 × 24 = 144000000 Bits

144000000 ÷ 8 = 18000 000 B

18000000 ÷ 1024 = 17578·125 Kb

17578·125 ÷ 1024 = 17·166 mb

(3 marks)

Sound

1 Sound can be represented digitally by taking samples of the original sound.

(a) State what is meant by sampling frequency.

Samples of a sound wave taken at regular intervals.

(1 mark)

(b) Describe the effect of increasing the sampling frequency.

A higher sampling frequency gives a more acurate reproduction of the sound.

(2 marks)

2 (a) Explain what is meant by the bit depth of a recording.

The number of bits used to encode each sample.

(2 marks)

(b) State the effect of increasing the bit depth of a recording.

Allows more data to be stored and allows more acurate representation **(1 mark)** _of sound_

3 The sampling frequency and bit depth affect the size of the file produced. Name **two** other factors which will affect the size of the file.

Factor 1 _Time Length_

Factor 2 _File Size_   **(2 marks)**

4 Construct an expression to calculate the file size, in megabytes, of a 100 second recording with a sampling frequency of 44.1 kHz if 16 bits are used to encode each sample.

> You should always show your working in questions involving calculations. You may get some credit for showing that you understand the method even if your final answer is wrong.

100 × 44100 × 16 = 70560000 bits

70560000 ÷ 8 = 8820000 bytes

_8820000 ÷ 1024 = 8613.281 KB_

_8613.281 ÷ 1024 = 8.411 MB_

(3 marks)

Had a go ☐   Nearly there ☐   Nailed it! ☐

Units

1 (a) State the format required for data to be processed by a computer.

.... **(1 mark)**

(b) Explain why instructions and data must be in this format.

....

....

.... **(2 marks)**

2 The following table shows the units of data storage capacity.
Complete the table to show the order of magnitude of the units, from smallest to largest.

Two have been filled in for you.

> Guided

byte	megabyte	terabyte	bit	kilobyte	gigabyte	nibble
3	5	7	1	4	6	2

(3 marks)

3 A file has a size of 72 000 000 000 bits.
Construct an expression to express this in megabytes.

$72,000,000,000 \div 8 = 900,000,000,0$ B

$900,000,000,0 \div 1024 = 8789062.5$ kb

$8789062.5 \div 1024 = 8583.06$ MB

(2 marks)

4 Construct an expression to show the number of bits in a file of size 20 terabytes.

$20 \times 1024 = 20480$ GB

$20480 \times 1024 = 20971520$ Mb

$20971520 \times 1024 = 2.147483648 \times 10^{10}$ kb

$2.147483648 \times 10^{10} \times 1024 = 2.199023256 \times 10^{13}$ B

$\times 8 =$

(1 mark)

Data compression

1 Leah is sending files to her brother Ollie, while he is away on holiday, by attaching them to emails. The files include images, music, and PDF and word-processed documents.

(a) Identify **two** advantages for Leah and Ollie of compressing the files.

1 ....

....

2 ....

.... **(2 marks)**

(b) Two types of compression are lossless and lossy.
Describe the difference between lossless and lossy compression.

....

....

....

....

....

....

....

.... **(4 marks)**

(c) State which type of compression is appropriate for each of the following files that Leah sends and explain why it is appropriate.

A PDF file of a novel.
Type of compression

....

Reason

....

....

....

Images of her trip to London.
Type of compression

....

Reason

....

....

.... **(4 marks)**

Run-length encoding

1 (a) Run-length encoding (RLE) is a compression algorithm that checks for redundancy in data files. Explain what is meant by redundancy in a data file.

....

....

....

.... **(2 marks)**

(b) Explain why run-length encoding would be more suitable for black and white image files rather than full colour ones.

....

....

....

.... **(2 marks)**

2 The following is a black and white image consisting of 36 pixels.

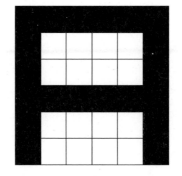

(a) Complete the table to show how the encoded data for this image can be compressed using run-length encoding.

Encode data	Compressed using run-length encoding
bbbbbb	
bwwwwb	
bwwwwb	
bbbbbb	
bwwwwb	
bwwwwb	

(3 marks)

(b) If one byte is needed to encode each character, state the number of characters needed before and after run-length encoding.

Before ....

After .... **(2 marks)**

Encryption

1 (a) Explain what is meant by data encryption.

....

....

....

.... **(2 marks)**

(b) Explain why data encryption is needed.

> You must make two valid points as there are two marks for this question.

....

....

....

.... **(2 marks)**

2 Complete the table using a Caesar cipher to encrypt the text.

> If you are unsure, check to see which way the letters are shifted for + and – or right and left shifts.

Plain text	Key	Cipher text
The battle is won	+ 3 or right 3	
Send more troops	– 3 or left 3	

(2 marks)

3 Complete the table to decrypt the cipher text that has been encrypted using a Caesar cipher.

> In this question you have to do the reverse of an encryption. The letters in the cipher text have been shifted and you must move them back.

Plain text	Key	Cipher text
Gzzgiq ot znk iktzxk	+ 6 or right 6	
Yofkd x elopb	– 3 or left 3	

(2 marks)

Structured and unstructured data

1 (a) Describe the difference between structured and unstructured data.

....

....

....

.... **(2 marks)**

(b) Explain the advantages to an organisation of ensuring that data is organised.

....

....

....

.... **(2 marks)**

2 Which **one** of the following is the best definition of an 'entity'?

☐ A   Any physical object

☐ B   A thing with an independent existence

☐ C   Any physical object or idea

☐ D   A thing with an independent existence about which data can be stored   **(1 mark)**

3 A student is creating a system to help run a school library where information about books borrowed by students can be stored.
List the **three** entities she could identify for this library system.

Entity 1 ....

Entity 2 ....

Entity 3 .... **(3 marks)**

4 A newsagent is creating a database to assist in newspaper deliveries. He has identified the following entities.

| Newspapers | Customers | Addresses | Delivery people |

| Daily delivery |

Draw arrowed lines on the diagram to show how these entities are related.   **(3 marks)**

Attributes and tables

1   Which of the following statements best defines what is meant by an attribute in a database?

   ☐   A   The properties of an entity
   ☐   B   Different examples of an entity
   ☐   C   A physical thing
   ☐   D   A link between entities   **(1 mark)**

2   A student who is creating a library database has identified 'Books' as an entity.
    Identify **three** suitable attributes of this entity.

> You are being asked to identify **three** suitable identifiable properties of this entity.

Attribute 1 ....

Attribute 2 ....

Attribute 3 ....   **(3 marks)**

3   A database has the following table.

B					
Car Make	**Model**	**Year**	**Colour**	**Fuel**	**Transmission**
Renault	Megane	2005	Black	Petrol	Manual
Hyundai	i20	2013	Red	Petrol	Manual
A Audi	A1	2015	Black	Petrol	Automatic

   (a)   Identify the (shaded) structures labelled A and B in the database table.

   A ....

   B ....   **(2 marks)**

   (b)   Each table must have a primary key.
         Explain what is meant by a primary field and why it is needed.

> There are **two** parts to this question. You are being asked to state what is meant by a key field and then say why it is required by the database software.

   ....

   ....

   ....

   ....   **(2 marks)**

   (c)   Explain why none of the fields in the table would make a suitable primary field
         and how the designers of the database could overcome this problem.

   ....

   ....

   ....

   ....   **(2 marks)**

Relational databases

1 Explain what is meant by a relational database.

> You are being asked to explain a specific type of database. So do **not** just give the general definition of a database.

....

....

....

.... **(2 marks)**

2 Which of the following statements best defines what is meant by a foreign key in a database?

☐ A A field in one database linked to the primary key of another database

☐ B A field in a table other than the primary key

☐ C A field in one table linked to the primary key of another

☐ D A field that is next to the primary key   **(1 mark)**

3 An organisation uses a relational database to keep track of orders.

tblStaff
Staff_Id
First_name
Surname
Department

tblOrders
Order_Number
Order_date
Customer_Id
Staff_Id

tblCustomers
Customer_Id
Customer_Name
Customer_Address

(a) Give **two** reasons for choosing to structure the business data.

1 ....

2 .... **(2 marks)**

(b) (i) The field Staff_Id has a specific function in tblStaff.
State the name of this specific function.

.... **(1 mark)**

(ii) The field Customer_Id has a specific function in tblOrders.
State the name of this specific function.

.... **(1 mark)**

(iii) The field Customer_Id in tblOrders has a specific function in the database.
State why this field is necessary.

.... **(1 mark)**

(c) Order_Number is a positive number, 8 bits in length.
Identify the range of values that can be represented.

.... **(1 mark)**

Input–processing–output

1 Complete the diagram by adding **six** arrows to indicate the input and output relationships between the devices.

	Visual Display Unit	
Secondary Storage	Central Processing Unit	Mouse
	Main Memory	

(3 marks)

2 One of the stages in the input–processing–output model is processing. Explain what is meant by 'processing'.

....

....

....

.... **(2 marks)**

Guided

3 Complete the table to indicate which stage of the input–processing–output model involves the following devices. One has been done for you.

Device	Stage
Keyboard	Input
Microphone	
Printer	
Central processing unit	
Speakers	
Monitor	

(2 marks)

The central processing unit

1   The table below shows some internal hardware components and their functions.

Complete the table below by filling in the missing information.

Internal hardware components	Function
CU (control unit)	
	Controls the rate at which program instructions are carried out.
ALU (arithmetic logic unit)	
	Stores frequently used program instructions and data so the processor isn't kept waiting for them to be transferred from the main memory.
Registers	

(5 marks)

2   Alva is buying a new laptop.

The sales assistant recommends one with a 3 GHz CPU.

He claims that it will always out-perform one with a 2 GHz CPU.

Explain why this may not be the case.

> You need to explain why the sales assistant would think that a 3 GHz processor will give better performance, but also mention other factors that can affect performance that Alva should consider.

....

....

....

....

....

....

....

....

....

....

....

....

.... **(6 marks)**

Components of the CPU

1 Explain what is meant by 'the Von Neumann model'.

....

....

....

.... **(2 marks)**

2 List **two** components with which the CPU works to execute program instructions.

> The question is asking about other components of the computer, not components of the CPU itself.

1 ....

2 .... **(2 marks)**

3 Describe the role of the CU (control unit) and the ALU (arithmetic logic unit) in the fetch–decode–execute cycle.

> This question is asking you to 'describe' and not just state the functions of the components. You must make at least two points about each one.

CU ....

....

....

....

ALU ....

....

....

.... **(4 marks)**

4 Within the CPU are memory locations called registers. Describe their role in the fetch–decode–execute cycle.

....

....

....

.... **(2 marks)**

5 Describe the role of the decoder in the fetch–decode–execute cycle.

....

....

....

.... **(2 marks)**

Fetch–decode–execute cycle

1 State the names of **two** buses involved in the fetch–decode–execute cycle and the role of each.

Bus 1 ....

....

....

....

Bus 2 ....

....

....

.... **(4 marks)**

2 The Von Neumann model carries out computer programs using the fetch–decode–execute cycle.

(a) The table below describes stages in the fetch–decode–execute cycle but they are not in order.
Write the numbers 1–4 in the empty cells to show the correct order.

Description	Order
The next instruction is sent from the RAM to the CPU.	
The instruction is carried out.	
The CU interprets the instruction.	
The CPU sends a signal to the RAM requesting the next instruction.	

(2 marks)

(b) State the role of RAM in the fetch–decode–execute cycle.

....

.... **(1 mark)**

(c) Annotate the diagram to show the role of the CU and ALU in the fetch–decode–execute cycle. **(2 marks)**

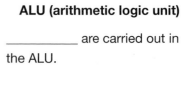

CU (control unit)

The CU _____ the instructions.
If a calculation is needed, the CU instructs the _____.

ALU (arithmetic logic unit)

_____ are carried out in the ALU.

Memory

1 The main memory of a computer consists of both volatile and non-volatile memory.

   (a) Define what is meant by 'volatile memory'.

   ....

   .... **(1 mark)**

   (b) State what non-volatile main memory is used for.

   ....

   .... **(1 mark)**

2 Complete this table by placing a tick in the column next to the **true** statements.

Statement	True
RAM stands for Random Access Memory	
ROM is volatile	
Data can be read from and written to ROM	
Program instructions and data are stored in RAM	
The sets of instructions needed for a computer to start are stored in ROM	

  (5 marks)

3 A computer's main memory consists of both RAM and ROM.
  Compare RAM and ROM.

> You have been asked to 'compare' RAM and ROM. Remember to refer to **both** of them for each difference or similarity. There are three marks for this question, so your answer should have three differences or similarities.

   ....

   ....

   ....

   ....

   ....

   .... **(3 marks)**

4 State **one** example of data which is stored in RAM.

   ....

   .... **(1 mark)**

Magnetic and optical storage

1 Most computer systems use at least one secondary storage device.

(a) Give **two** reasons why a secondary storage device is needed in most computer systems.

1 ....

....

2 ....

.... **(2 marks)**

(b) Some secondary storage devices are magnetic and some are optical.

> These questions ask you to 'describe' how data is stored on magnetic and optical drives. You will not gain the marks by just stating that the data is stored 'by magnetism' or 'by laser'; you will need to describe the structure of the devices and explain how the data is written and read.

   (i) Describe how data is stored on magnetic storage devices.

   ....

   ....

   ....

   .... **(2 marks)**

   (ii) Describe how data is stored on optical storage devices.

   ....

   ....

   ....

   .... **(2 marks)**

(c) Explain why magnetic devices are used in preference to optical ones as the main storage devices in most computer systems.

> This question is worth 2 marks so your answer should include two different points and should include a justification.

....

....

....

.... **(2 marks)**

2 Noah has 200 photos that he wants to put on a CD or DVD. Each photo is 8 MB in size. Calculate whether all his photos can be saved on a single CD or on a single DVD.

....

....

....

.... **(2 marks)**

Solid-state memory

1 Describe how data is stored on a solid-state drive.

....

....

....

Internal hardware components

....

....   **(3 marks)**

2 An SD card is an example of a solid-state storage device.

(a) Give **one** reason why it is called a 'solid-state' storage device.

....

....   **(1 mark)**

(b) Apart from SD cards, state **two** other uses of solid-state storage.

1 ....

....

2 ....

....   **(2 marks)**

3 Complete the table with the names of the category of secondary storage described in each row.

> It is a category of storage that is needed, not a type of storage device. Responses such as 'hard disc', 'CD' or 'flash drive' will not gain any mark.

Category of secondary storage	Description
	Uses metal platters coated in iron oxide. The platters rotate at high speed.
	Small pits are burned in patterns onto a flat surface. A laser can be used to interpret light reflected from the flat or pitted surface.
	No moving parts; data is stored as an electrical charge.

(3 marks)

4 Gloria has removed the hard disk drive from her laptop and replaced it with a solid-state drive.
Give **two** reasons why this is a suitable upgrade.

....

....

....

....   **(2 marks)**

Cloud storage

1   Many organisations now store and back up their data using cloud storage rather than to devices connected to their servers.

(a)   Explain what is meant by 'cloud storage'.

....

....

....

....   **(2 marks)**

(b)   When saving data, compare the use of cloud storage with devices connected to a local server.

> You are being asked to compare the two methods and so you should not just list the advantages and disadvantages of each method.

....

....

....

....

....

....

....

....

....

....

....

....

....

....

....

....

....

....   **(6 marks)**

Embedded systems

1 (a) Elaine has been told that her digital camera is controlled by an embedded system.
        Define what is meant by an 'embedded system'.

....

.... **(1 mark)**

   (b) Identify **three** components of an embedded system.

   > You have been asked to 'identify' components. There are more possibilities than you have
   > been asked for.

   1 ....

   2 ....

   3 .... **(3 marks)**

   (c) List **two** other devices that contain embedded systems.

....

.... **(2 marks)**

2 Desktop computers are referred to as 'general purpose machines' and embedded
   systems are called 'special purpose machines'.

   (a) Explain the difference between these two types of system.

....

....

....

.... **(2 marks)**

   (b) Explain why embedded systems are also referred to as 'real-time' systems.

....

....

....

.... **(2 marks)**

   (c) Explain why low-level languages such as
        assembly language are used for writing
        the programs for embedded systems.

   > For a reminder on assembly language,
   > look at page 63 of the Revision Guide.

....

....

....

.... **(2 marks)**

Logic

1 Truth tables are used to show how digital output relates to input.

(a) Complete the truth table for the OR statement.

INPUT		OUTPUT
0	0	

(3 marks)

(b) Complete the truth table for the NOT statement.

INPUT	OUTPUT

(2 marks)

2 Complete the truth table for the following logic statement.
P = A AND NOT(B)

> Remember that the NOT operator reverses the logic of the AND statement.

A	B	P

(4 marks)

3 Complete the truth table for the following logic statement.
P = NOT(A OR B) AND NOT(C)

A	B	C	P

(4 marks)

Logic circuits

1 A conveyor belt in a factory can be turned on by either switch A or switch B.
To ensure the safety of the workers there is also an override switch which must be
in the off position before the belt will move.

(a) Construct a logic statement to represent the logic of this behaviour, using the
symbols A, B and C.

....

.... **(2 marks)**

(b) Complete the truth table for this statement where P represents the movement of
the belt.

A	B	C	P

(4 marks)

2 An automatic watering system for a greenhouse uses a light sensor (A) and a moisture sensor
(B), which will emit a signal when the soil is wet, to ensure that the sprinklers (P) are turned on
only at night and only when the soil is dry.

(a) Create a logic statement for this system.

....

.... **(2 marks)**

(b) Complete the truth table for this statement.

A	B	P

(2 marks)

Operating system 1

1 Describe the role of systems software in a computer system.

> You are expected to give a general overview of 'systems software'.

....

....

....

.... **(2 marks)**

2 (a) Explain the role of the operating system in memory management and multitasking.

> Use the number of marks as a guide to how much to write. Part (a) is worth 4 marks, and parts (b) and (c) are worth 2 marks each, so your answer to part (a) should be longer than your answers to parts (b) and (c).

....

....

....

....

....

....

....

.... **(4 marks)**

(b) Explain why file management is used.

....

....

....

.... **(2 marks)**

(c) Explain how file permissions are used on shared computer systems or on a network.

....

....

....

.... **(2 marks)**

Operating system 2

1 Two of the functions of the operating system are to manage the computer users and provide an interface between them and the hardware and software of the computer system.

> Even though these functions are linked, you must comment on both.
>
> In your answer, you should avoid simply rewriting information already given in the question. This will save you time in the exam. For example, you would not get a mark for writing 'On shared computers, the operating system manages users.'
>
> Make sure you read the question properly and only write relevant information.

(a) Explain how an operating system manages computer users.

....

....

....

....

....

.... **(3 marks)**

(b) Explain how an operating system provides an interface between computer users and the hardware and software of the computer system.

....

....

....

....

....

.... **(3 marks)**

2 Peripheral devices are used to input data and output information into and out of a computer system.

Explain how the operating system manages peripheral devices.

....

....

....

.... **(2 marks)**

Utility software 1

1   Stephen's computer is running slowly and he thinks it's because his hard disk drive is fragmented.

(a)   State what is meant by 'fragmented'.

....

.... **(1 mark)**

(b)   Explain how defragmentation software will help to make the computer run more quickly.

....

....

....

.... **(2 marks)**

(c)   Stephen is advised to use data compression software to create more space on his hard disk drive.

(i)   Give another instance when Stephen should use compression software.

....

.... **(1 mark)**

(ii)   Describe the difference between lossless and lossy compression.

....

....

....

.... **(2 marks)**

(d)   Stephen wants to make copies of all of his programs and files using backup software. The software allows Stephen to make a full backup whenever he wants.

(i)   State the name of a different backup strategy that Stephen could use.

.... **(1 mark)**

(ii)   Explain how this method should reduce the time spent on backing up.

....

....

....

.... **(2 marks)**

2   Explain why encryption software is used.

....

....

....

.... **(2 marks)**

Utility software 2

1 Any software that has been designed to gain unauthorised access to a computer system in order to disrupt its functioning or collect information is an example of:

☐ A   a virus program

☐ B   a malware program

☐ C   a trojan program

☐ D   a spyware program.   **(1 mark)**

2 Viruses and spyware are both examples of malware.
Describe how a computer system can be infected by each one and the harm that it can do.

(a) Virus ....

....

....

.... **(2 marks)**

(b) Spyware ....

....

....

.... **(2 marks)**

3 Anti-virus software is a type of utility software.
Describe **two** methods that this software uses to identify malware.

....

....

....

....

....

....

....

.... **(4 marks)**

4 Stephen transfers a video from his computer to his tablet but the media player will not accept it.
He should use:

☐ A   anti-malware software

☐ B   file repair software

☐ C   file conversion software

☐ D   anti-virus software.   **(1 mark)**

Simulation and modelling

1 Catherine is making a computer model of her finances.

(a) Explain what is meant by a 'computer model'.

....

....

....

.... **(2 marks)**

(b) State **two** other examples of computer models, other than financial models.

> You have been asked to state two examples, so you just need to name them and do not need to describe them. Make sure you give models other than financial models.

Example 1 ....

Example 2 .... **(2 marks)**

(c) Computer models are widely used in all industries.
Explain **two** advantages to those industries of using computer models.

> You are being asked to explain the advantages and so a one-word answer will not be sufficient to obtain the marks available.

Advantage 1 ....

....

....

Advantage 2 ....

....

....

.... **(4 marks)**

(d) Describe **two** drawbacks of creating and using computer models.

Drawback 1 ....

....

....

....

Drawback 2 ....

....

....

.... **(4 marks)**

Programming languages

1 The same program has been written in three different languages, as shown below.

> You need to be able to recognise low- and high-level languages and the form in which they are written.

Language 1	Language 2	Language 3
firstNumber = 1 secondNumber = 2 total = a + b	LD 1 ADD 2 STORE 3	00111110 00000001 00000110 00000010 10000000

(a) State the name of Language 2. .... **(1 mark)**

(b) State the name of Language 3. .... **(1 mark)**

(c) Explain why Language 1 is a high-level language, while Languages 2 and 3 are low-level languages.

....

....

....

.... **(2 marks)**

(d) (i) Describe **two** advantages for a programmer of writing programs in a high-level language.

1 ....

....

....

2 ....

....

.... **(4 marks)**

(ii) Describe **two** advantages for a programmer of writing programs in a low-level language.

1 ....

....

....

2 ....

....

.... **(4 marks)**

Translators

1 Computers can only execute instructions written in machine code.

(a) State the name of the software used to translate a program written in assembly language into machine code.

....

.... **(1 mark)**

(b) Both compilers and interpreters translate high-level program code into machine code.
Compare the method of translation used by each.

....

....

....

.... **(2 marks)**

(c) Outline **one** advantage and **one** disadvantage of each method for programmers and users.

Compiler

....

....

....

....

Interpreter

....

....

....

.... **(4 marks)**

2 A programmer is writing software for a new set-top receiver for satellite TV.
Explain why the programmer should use a compiler instead of an interpreter to translate the code.

....

.... **(2 marks)**

LANs and WANs

1 A small business has six standalone computers, a printer and an internet connection in an office. The office manager is thinking of linking the computers to form a network.

(a) Describe what is meant by a network.

....

....

....

.... **(2 marks)**

(b) State **two** advantages of connecting the computers to form a network.

1 ....

....

2 ....

.... **(2 marks)**

> You are being asked to 'describe' the characteristics of a LAN and a WAN so don't just state what each one is. You must describe some of the features of each one. Use the number of marks as a guide for the number of points you need to make.

2 Two types of network are a LAN (local area network) and a WAN (wide area network).

(a) Describe the characteristics of a LAN.

....

....

....

....

....

.... **(3 marks)**

(b) Describe the characteristics of a WAN.

....

....

....

....

....

.... **(3 marks)**

Client–server and peer-to-peer networks

1　A computer consultant, giving advice on office networks, suggested that a small company with only six computers should install a peer-to-peer network but suggested that a large company with over one hundred computers should install a client–server network.

> Make sure you read each question carefully.

(a)　Describe the characteristics of a 'peer-to-peer' network.

....

....

....

....

....

.... **(3 marks)**

(b)　Explain **two** benefits to the small company of installing a peer-to-peer network rather than a client–server one.

> You are **not** being asked about the benefits of using a network but about the benefits to a small company of installing a peer-to-peer network rather than a client–server network.

1 ....

....

....

....

2 ....

....

....

.... **(4 marks)**

(c)　The consultant advised the large company to install a client–server network. Give **two** reasons why the consultant might have given this advice.

1 ....

....

....

....

2 ....

....

....

.... **(4 marks)**

Wired and wireless connectivity

1 Devices on a network communicate using copper wired cable or fibre optic cable.

(a) Compare the method of data transmission in the two types of cable.

> When you compare two items you must specifically refer to them by name in the answer.

....

....

.... **(2 marks)**

(b) State **one** advantage and **one** disadvantage of using fibre optic cable rather than copper cable.

Advantage

....

Disadvantage

.... **(2 marks)**

2 Network data can be transmitted over wireless networks using radio waves.

(a) State the range of frequencies commonly used for data transmission in wireless networks.

.... **(1 mark)**

(b) A network device is advertised as transmitting on channel 6. Explain what is meant by a channel.

....

....

.... **(2 marks)**

3 Compare the use of cable or wireless as the transmission medium by considering:

(a) Security

....

....

(b) Interference

....

....

(c) Bandwidth

....

.... **(6 marks)**

Connecting computers to a LAN

On this page there are 'describe' and 'explain' questions with 2, 3 or 4 marks. These questions require you to make several points in the answer. The first one has been done for you as an example.

1 (a) Describe the role of NICs (network interface controllers) in connecting devices to computer networks.

> There are 2 marks for this question so two points should be made in the description.

Guided

A NIC provides a physical connection to either a wired or a wireless network for

a device on the network. The NIC formats the data so that it can be transmitted

and received across the network. **(2 marks)**

(b) Explain how each NIC is uniquely identified and addressed on the network.

....

....

.... **(2 marks)**

2 Devices on a network can be linked using switches.
Explain why using a switch to connect devices on a network is preferable to using a hub.

....

....

....

.... **(3 marks)**

3 When Anika takes her laptop to school, she can connect it without using a cable to the school's cable network.

(a) State the role of a wireless access point in a network.

.... **(1 mark)**

(b) Anika's family has a home network.
Explain the role of the router in Anika's home network.

> There are 4 marks for this question, so you cannot just say 'it connects networks together'. You must name the networks that are being connected and explain how the router ensures that all members of the household receive the correct data.

....

....

....

....

....

.... **(4 marks)**

Data transmission

1   When data is transmitted across a network it is split into packets.

(a) State **one** reason why data is split into packets.

....

.... **(1 mark)**

(b) Give **three** components of each packet and state one function of each.

Component 1 ....

Function ....

....

Component 2 ....

Function ....

....

Component 3 ....

Function ....

.... **(6 marks)**

2   The following table shows the layers of the TCP/IP protocol stack, the purpose of each layer and **one** protocol in each layer.
Complete the table.

Name of layer	Purpose	One protocol in the layer
Application layer		HTTP
	Divides data sent from application layer into packets. Checks that data sent has been received and notifies sender that data has been received.	
Internet layer		
		Ethernet

(5 marks)

Protocols

1 When computers on a network communicate with each other they need to use the same protocols.

(a) Describe **three** functions of protocols in controlling how data is sent across networks.

1 ....

....

2 ....

....

3 ....

.... **(6 marks)**

(b) This table lists some of the protocols used by computers when communicating over the internet.
Complete the table by inserting the protocol next to its function. The first one has been done for you.

⟩ **Guided** ⟩

Protocol	Function
HTTPS	Used when communications between a client and host have to be encrypted.
	Provides the rules for sending email messages from client to server and then from server to server until they reach their destination.
	Provides the rules to be followed by web browsers when accessing the internet and by web servers when requesting and supplying information.
	Provides the rules for transferring files between computers.

(3 marks)

(c) Two protocols used in networks are TCP and IP.

(i) State what the initials TCP and IP stand for.

....

.... **(1 mark)**

(ii) Describe the functions of these two protocols.

TCP

....

....

....

IP

....

....

.... **(4 marks)**

Network topologies 1

1 A small business is going to connect its standalone computers together using a star topology.

> You need to draw an annotated diagram with descriptions of the components.

  (a) With the aid of a diagram, describe a star topology.

(2 marks)

  (b) Give **three** reasons why the business would choose to use a star topology.

1 ....

....

....

....

2 ....

....

....

....

3 ....

....

....

.... **(3 marks)**

Network topologies 2

1 Ring and bus are examples of network topologies.

(a) Draw and label diagrams to illustrate these topologies.

> You can represent a computer by a box, as long as you label it. You do not have to draw a diagram of a computer.

Ring topology	Bus topology

(4 marks)

(b) One advantage of a ring network over a bus network is that there are no data collisions.

(i) Explain what is meant by a data collision.

....

....

....

.... **(2 marks)**

(ii) Explain why there are no data collisions on a ring network.

....

....

....

.... **(2 marks)**

2 The table shows characteristics of different network topologies.
Complete the table.

Network topology	Characteristic
	Each device is connected to a central switch.
	Each device is connected to a central cable with a T-piece.
	Each device has a dedicated connection to all other devices on the network.
	Nodes cooperate to take turns sending data.

(4 marks)

Network security 1

1   The security of their network is vitally important for all organisations.
Suggest the reasons for network security and why it is so important for organisations.

> Your answer should demonstrate comprehensive knowledge and understanding by selecting relevant knowledge and understanding of key concepts and principles of computer science to support the discussion being presented. Think about what you want to say and make a plan before you start writing your answer.
>
> You might find it useful to use headings to remind you of the different topics you need to write about. Your reasons should be given in a sensible ordered sequence rather than being random.

....

....

....

....

....

....

....

....

....

....

.... **(6 marks)**

2   (a)   One method of implementing network security is the validation of users by the use of passwords.
Give **three** rules that users should follow when creating and using passwords.

Rule 1 ....

....

Rule 2 ....

....

Rule 3 ....

.... **(3 marks)**

(b)   Explain how access control is used to help ensure network security.

....

....

....

.... **(3 marks)**

Network security 2

1   An organisation is planning a new network and computer suite for its main site where data that is essential for the running of the whole organisation is stored and processed.

   (a)   Describe three physical security measures that the organisation could implement to ensure the safety of their suite and help to prevent unauthorised access.

> You are being asked to describe the security measures and therefore you should write about each method rather than just stating the name of each one.

Measure 1 ....

....

....

Measure 2 ....

....

....

Measure 3 ....

....

....   **(6 marks)**

   (b)   A firewall can help to prevent unauthorised access of data stored on the network.

   Explain how a firewall is used to do this.

> There are four marks for this question and you should mention the types of firewall and how they prevent unauthorised access.

....

....

....

....

....

....

....   **(4 marks)**

Cyberattacks

1   Cyberattacks often target the users of a system, using social engineering techniques rather than any technical weaknesses in security.

Describe **two** social engineering techniques used by hackers.

Technique 1 ....

....

....

....

Technique 2 ....

....

....

.... **(4 marks)**

2   An organisation is concerned that its network communications are being intercepted and the information is being sold to a rival company.

(a)   State the name for this type of cyberattack.

....

.... **(1 mark)**

(b)   Explain how this type of cyberattack is carried out.

....

....

....

.... **(2 marks)**

(c)   State **one** precaution that the organisation should take to ensure any intercepted data is of no value to the hackers.

....

.... **(1 mark)**

3   Explain why the proliferation of smart devices in the home is providing opportunities for hackers to launch cyberattacks.

....

....

....

.... **(2 marks)**

Identifying vulnerabilities

1 (a) Jamail has started work at a new company and has been asked to read and sign the network policies.

All companies should have network policies and should review them frequently.

State **three** items that should be covered in a company's network policies.

> The question asks you to 'state' three items so explanations are not required.

1 ....

....

2 ....

....

3 ....

.... **(3 marks)**

(b) The company has asked a team of consultants to assess its network security by carrying out a penetration test.

Explain the role of penetration testing in assessing network security.

> You are being asked to 'explain' so just saying what a penetration test is will not be sufficient to obtain the 2 marks.

....

....

....

.... **(2 marks)**

(c) The consultants also used commercial analysis tools to assess the security of the network.

Explain the role of commercial analysis tools.

....

....

....

.... **(2 marks)**

(d) The company has been contacted by an ethical hacker regarding their network security.

Explain what is meant by 'ethical hacking'.

....

....

.... **(2 marks)**

Protecting software systems

1 State three security issues that programmers should consider when they are designing new software.

> The question asks you to 'state' three items so explanations are not required.

1 ....

....

2 ....

....

3 ....

.... **(3 marks)**

2 Describe **two** ways in which security flaws in software can be identified and removed when a program is being designed and coded.

Method 1 ....

....

....

Method 2 ....

....

....

.... **(4 marks)**

3 Describe the importance of audit trails in network security.

....

....

....

.... **(2 marks)**

4 Alice has set the operating system of her laptop to automatic update.

Explain why this is good practice.

....

....

....

.... **(2 marks)**

The internet

1 Ayana is using her computer to access the internet.

(a) Explain why Ayana will need to select an ISP (internet service provider).

....

....

....

.... **(2 marks)**

(b) The ISP provides Ayana's computer with an IP address.

(i) Explain why Ayana's computer needs an IP address.

....

....

....

.... **(2 marks)**

(ii) Compare the structure of IPv4 and IPv6 addresses.

....

....

....

.... **(2 marks)**

2 Data is transmitted on the internet in packets.

(a) Explain what is meant by a 'packet'.

....

....

....

.... **(2 marks)**

(b) Describe how the packets are transmitted across the internet and the role of routers.

....

....

....

....

.... **(4 marks)**

The world wide web

1 Lianne is using the world wide web to find information for her homework.

(a) Explain what is meant by the world wide web (WWW).

> This requires a precise definition explaining the pages of information, where they are stored and how they are connected.

....

....

....

.... **(2 marks)**

(b) State the name of the scripting language used for creating web pages.

....

.... **(1 mark)**

(c) Name **one** protocol that Lianne's computer uses to access information on the WWW.

....

.... **(1 mark)**

(d) When Lianne enters the address of a website she wants to visit, she enters its URL rather than its IP address.

Explain why URLs are used instead of IP addresses.

....

....

....

.... **(2 marks)**

(e) Explain the role of the Domain Name Service when Lianne requests access to a website.

....

....

....

....

....

....

.... **(4 marks)**

Environmental issues

1   Discuss the positive and negative effects of computer science technology on the environment.

> Remember that you will need an introduction and a conclusion.
>
> Think about what you want to say and make a plan before you start writing your answer. You might find it useful to use headings to remind you of the different topics you need to write about.
>
> Your arguments should be given in a sensibly ordered sequence rather than being random.

....

....

....

....

....

....

....

....

....

....

....

....

....

....

....

....

....

....

....

....

....

....

....

.... **(6 marks)**

Ethical impact

1   People often argue that many developments in technology allow or encourage behaviour that is not ethical.

(a)   State what is meant by 'ethical behaviour'.

....

.... **(1 mark)**

(b)   One ethical consideration is often referred to as the 'digital divide'.

(i)   Explain what is meant by the 'digital divide'.

....

....

....

.... **(2 marks)**

(ii) Describe the negative impact on society of the digital divide and ways in which technology has had positive impacts on social inclusion.

....

....

....

....

....

....

....

....

.... **(6 marks)**

2   A computer scientist has several client companies, both large and small. When she gets requests for assistance and to fix bugs in her software, she has to prioritise how she responds. She could:

1   solve each one as it is received

2   solve the ones for the large companies first as they pay more money

3   decide which are the most serious and solve them first.

Discuss these options with regard to working in an ethical way.

....

....

....

....

....

.... **(4 marks)**

Privacy issues

1   Many people assert that some uses of computer science technology have infringed their right to privacy but others argues that they are beneficial for society.

Discuss how some uses of computer science technology have an impact on an individual's privacy and how these could also be beneficial for society.

> You could start by making a list of the uses of some relevant computer science technologies, for example surveillance cameras. You then need to consider the impact these have on a person's privacy as well as their benefits.

....

....

....

....

....

....

....

....

....

....

....

....

....

....

....

....

....

....

....

....

....

....

....

.... **(6 marks)**

Legislation

1   The Copyright, Designs and Patents Act (1988) is intended to protect the rights of certain individuals.

(a)   What kinds of work are protected under this Act?

....

....   **(1 mark)**

(b)   Who owns the copyright of the work?

....

....   **(1 mark)**

(c)   If internet users illegally download works covered by the Act, legal sanctions can be taken against them.

List **two** of the sanctions.

1 ....

2 ....   **(2 marks)**

2   Some copyright holders grant users of their works Creative Commons licences.

Give **two** reasons why a content creator might consider using a Creative Commons licence to make their work available to others.

1 ....

....

2 ....

....   **(2 marks)**

3   The Computer Misuse Act 1990 identifies three types of offence:
A   Unauthorised access to computer material.
B   Unauthorised modification of computer material.
C   Unauthorised access with intent to commit further offences.

The table below lists some actions that take place in a school.
Complete the table by entering A, B or C in the box beside each action to state the type of offence being committed.

Action	Type of offence
A student accesses another student's email account without permission.	
A user accesses parents' stored credit card numbers and security codes in order to buy goods online fraudulently.	
A student guesses the login names and passwords of other students and logs into their accounts.	
A student gains access to class results and changes their own marks and grades.	
As a challenge, a student manages to guess the password of one of the administrative staff to gain entry to the management system.	

(5 marks)

Proprietary and open-source software

1   TicToc manufactures smart watches. It uses proprietary software to develop apps for the watch.

(a) What is meant by 'proprietary software'?

....

.... **(1 mark)**

(b) Explain **one** advantage to TicToc of using proprietary software rather than open-source software to develop apps.

....

....

....

.... **(2 marks)**

(c) TicToc is considering using open-source software to develop its apps instead of proprietary software.
Describe **one** benefit to users of the smart watch if TicToc decides to use open-source software.

....

....

....

.... **(2 marks)**

2   This table shows some statements about proprietary and open-source software.
Tick the column to show whether the statements apply to proprietary or open-source software.

Statement	Proprietary	Open-source
The source code cannot be modified by anyone except the person, team or organisation that created it.		
It is free to use.		
Users can modify the source code to adapt it to their needs and can pass it on to other users free of charge.		
The software must be paid for.		
Users can study the source code to see how the software works.		
It may need specialist knowledge to install the software.		
The support and updates may be expensive.		
The software will be developed carefully and tested thoroughly because people will be paying money to use it and they will be cross if it doesn't work.		
There is a community of dedicated enthusiasts who will provide help and support.		

(4 marks)

Practice Paper 1
Principles of computer science

Answer ALL questions. Write your answers in the spaces provided.

1   Jamila has just bought a new laptop.

Figure 1

The laptop was advertised as having a 2.6 GHz CPU with a 6 megabyte cache, 16 gigabytes of RAM and a 512 gigabyte solid state drive.

(a)   The role of the CPU is to process program instructions using the fetch–decode–execute cycle.

Complete the table to give the role of the following components of the CPU in this cycle.

(6)

Component	Function
CU (control unit)	
Address bus	
Clock	
Registers	
ALU (arithmetic logic unit)	
Data bus	

(b) In addition to RAM, the laptop's memory also contains ROM.

Tick one box in each row of the table to show whether each of the statements is true for ROM or RAM. **(3)**

	RAM	ROM
Program instructions and data are stored here		
It is used to boot up the laptop when it is switched on		
It is volatile		

(c) The CPU has 6 megabytes of cache memory.

Explain how the cache improves the performance of the processor. **(2)**

....

....

....

....

(d) Identify the type of secondary storage used by the computer. **(1)**

☐   A   Magnetic storage

☐   B   Optical storage

☐   C   Electrical storage

☐   D   Dynamic storage

(Total for Question 1 = 12 marks)

2   A design company with 100 employees has decided to install a network to improve communications and productivity.

They have decided to use a client–server network with a star topology.

(a) Draw and label a diagram to show how the computers and any required equipment could be connected using a star topology. **(3)**

(b) Describe **two** roles of a server in a client–server network. **(4)**

Role 1 ....

....

....

....

Role 2 ....

....

....

....

(c) (i) When computers communicate with each other on a network they must use the same protocol.

State what is meant by a 'protocol'. **(2)**

....

....

....

....

(ii) Identify a network protocol that is used for data transmission on a local area network. **(1)**

☐ A   HTTP

☐ B   SMTP

☐ C   TCP/IP

☐ D   Ethernet

(d) Describe validation and authentication techniques that could be used to ensure the security of a network. **(6)**

....

....

....

....

....

....

....

....

(Total for Question 2 = 16 marks)

3   A team of programmers is developing an online game that can be played on different devices including computers, tablets and smartphones.

(a)   The program is being written in a high-level language and then translated into machine code.

(i)   Describe **two** differences between high-level code and machine code.   **(4)**

1 ....

....

....

....

2 ....

....

....

....

(ii)   Explain **two** advantages to the team of using a high-level language to develop the game.   **(4)**

1 ....

....

....

....

2 ....

....

....

....

(b)   One type of translator to convert high-level to machine code is an interpreter.

(i)   Describe how an interpreter converts high-level code to machine code.   **(2)**

....

....

....

....

(ii)   State the name of a different type of translator which can be used to convert high-level code to machine code.   **(1)**

....

(Total for Question 3 = 11 marks)

4 (a) Explain why data is stored in computers in a binary format. **(2)**

....

....

....

....

(b) (i) Add the following two 8-bit binary numbers. **(2)**

```
1  0  1  1  1  0  1  1
0  1  1  0  1  0  1  0
```
_____

_____

(ii) State the name of the error that has occurred when adding these two binary numbers. **(1)**

....

(c) Convert the binary number 10111011 to decimal, showing your working. **(2)**

....

....

....

....

(d) True-colour colour codes consist of three 8-bit numbers. The code for Ferrari red is shown below.

11110111   00001101   00011010

Programmers prefer to use hexadecimal to enter the codes into programs.

(i) When the binary code is converted into hexadecimal some of the digits are shown below.

Complete the table to show the first two digits. **(2)**

Binary	11110111	00001101	00011010
Hexadecimal		0D	1A

(ii) Explain why programmers prefer to use hexadecimal. **(2)**

....

....

....

....

(Total for Question 4 = 11 marks)

5   Figure 2 is a bitmap image that Ann took with her camera during her trip to the seaside and downloaded to her laptop.

Figure 2

(a) The operating system gives the properties of the image as having a width of 4288 and a height of 2484 and a colour depth of 24.

   (i) State the units in which the width and height are measured.   **(1)**

   ....

   (ii) Explain what is meant by 'colour depth'.   **(2)**

   ....

   ....

   ....

   ....

   (iii) Construct an expression to calculate the size of the image file in megabytes. You do not need to carry out the calculation.   **(4)**

   ....

   ....

   ....

   ....

(b) Lossy compression algorithms are often used to reduce the files sizes of image files.

   (i) Explain what is meant by 'lossy compression'.   **(2)**

   ....

   ....

   ....

   ....

   (ii) Explain why these algorithms are suitable for image files but should not be used to reduce the sizes of text files.   **(2)**

   ....

   ....

   ....

   ....

(Total for Question 5 = 11 marks)

6 Stephen has stored the names of the countries he has visited in an array named 'countries'.

Part of the data is shown in Figure 3.

Figure 3

Peru	Laos	Cambodia	India	Australia	Nepal

(a) Explain why an array is a suitable data structure to store this data.   **(2)**

....

....

....

....

(b) Show the stages of a bubble sort when applied to the data shown in Figure 3 to sort them into ascending order.   **(3)**

....

....

....

....

....

....

(c) After the sort, the countries are in the order shown in Figure 4.

Figure 4

Australia	Cambodia	India	Laos	Nepal	Peru

Give the sequence of values visited to find Peru using a binary search.   **(3)**

....

....

(Total for Question 6 = 8 marks)

7 (a) Complete a truth table for the logic statement P = (A AND B) OR C **(4)**

A	B	C	P

(b) The launch of a missile has the following control system to ensure it is not launched without authorisation.

A No-Launch switch (N) is permanently switched on and the missile will not launch until it is switched off. Two independent operators must also both turn switches A and B to their 'on' positions.

(i) Construct a logic statement to represent the logic of this behaviour, using the symbols N, A and B. **(2)**

....

....

(ii) Complete a truth table for the statement using L for the launch of the missile. **(4)**

(Total for Question 6 = 10 marks)

Practice Paper 2
Application of computational thinking

Answer ALL questions. Write your answers in the spaces provided.
Questions in this paper are based on a scenario.

WeDriveAnyWhere

WeDriveAnyWhere is a taxi firm based in a town near London.

Customers can phone or hail one of the taxis outside local railway stations and town and shopping centres.

They also offer airport trips and offer contracts for regular users so that they can obtain discounts.

They have a fixed number of full-time drivers and part-timers who they can call on when there is greatest demand.

They charge customers according to the distance, the time of day, the time taken and the number of passengers.

Drivers are paid according to the number of trips they make and the distance they drive.

---

1 Computer programs are used to store data about the journeys.

(a) Identify **two** variables from the scenario that need to be created to store this data. **(2)**

1 ....

2 ....

(b) Local journeys are charged at a basic rate of £3 plus 50 pence per mile and 20 pence per minute.

Construct a general expression to calculate the cost of each journey. **(2)**

....

....

....

....

....

(c) A computer program can be used to determine information about the journeys and the drivers.

Complete the table to show an input, a process and an output. **(3)**

Input	Process	Output
	Sum times for each journey	Total time driven
Total money taken during the day		Mean charge per journey
Number of drivers on duty	Number of trips/Number of drivers on duty	

(Total for Question 1 = 7 marks)

2   WeDriveAnyWhere employs part-time drivers according to the number of journeys they expect each day.

An algorithm is used to calculate this. Part of it is shown below.

1	`SET days TO [300, 700, 600, 700, 800, 1000, 1500]`
2	`WHILE use = 'yes' DO`
3	`    SEND 'Enter day number (Sunday = 0)' TO DISPLAY`
4	`    RECEIVE dayNumber FROM (INTEGER) KEYBOARD`
5	`    SET journeys TO days[dayNUMBER]`
6	`    SET driversNeeded TO journeys DIV 60`
8	`    SET partTime TO driversNeeded - 3`
9	
10	`    SEND 'Do you want to enter another day (yes or no)?' TO DISPLAY`
11	`    RECEIVE use FROM (STRING) KEYBOARD`
12	`END WHILE`

(a) State how many journeys are expected on Thursday.   **(1)**

....

(b) The algorithm has a logical error.

Identify this error and explain how it could be corrected.   **(2)**

....

....

....

....

(c) (i) There is a further error in the algorithm.

State the line number of this error and what the error is.   **(2)**

Line number ....

Error ....

....

(ii) State what this type of error is called.   **(1)**

....

....

(d) (i) State the number of journeys that each driver is expected to make each day.   **(1)**

....

(ii) Explain why the DIV operator has been used on line 6.   **(2)**

....

....

....

....

(e) Complete line 9 so that a sentence is displayed on the monitor stating the number of part time drivers required, like this.

The number of part-time drivers required is ***

(2)

....

....

....

....

(f) Using the algorithm, calculate how many part-time staff will be needed on Thursday.

(2)

....

....

(Total for Question 2 = 13 marks)

3 A program has been written for the drivers to keep track of the number of their journeys and the times taken using the following algorithm.

1	#This is the main program
2	SET totalTime TO 0
3	SET numberJourneys TO 0
4	SET repeat TO 'y'
5	WHILE repeat = 'y' DO
6	SET journeyTime, repeat TO elapsedTime()
7	SET totalTime TO totalTime + journeyTime
8	SET numberJourneys TO numberJourneys + 1
9	SEND 'You have driven ' & numberJourneys & ' for ' & totalTime
10	END WHILE
11	SEND 'Hope you enjoyed your shift.' TO DISPLAY
12	#This is a function
13	FUNCTION elapsedTime()
14	BEGIN FUNCTION
15	SET startTime TO getTime() #The getTime() function returns the current time when the driver presses a button at the start of the journey
16	SET endTime TO getTime() #The getTime() function returns the time again when the driver presses the button at the end of the journey.
17	SET tripTime TO endTime – startTime
18	SEND 'Are you going to drive another journey? ('y' or 'n')' TO DISPLAY
19	RECEIVE reply FROM KEYBOARD #The data type has deliberately not been stated.
20	RETURN tripTime, reply
21	END FUNCTION

(a) Complete the table to identify **one** line number for each feature of the program.   **(3)**

Feature	Line number
Iteration	
Comment	
Indentation	

(b) (i) Complete the table which lists variables and their data types.   **(3)**

Variable	Data type
	integer
tripTime	
repeat	

(ii) State **one** example of **one** global and **one** local variable used in the algorithm.   **(2)**

Global variable ....

Local variable ....

(c) The programmer has used a subprogram within the program.

   (i) State **two** benefits of using subprograms within programs.   **(2)**

     Benefit 1 ....

     Benefit 2 ....

   (ii) The type of subprogram used in this algorithm is a function.

     State the name of another type of subprogram and state how it is different to a function.   **(2)**

     Type of subprogram ....

     How it is different ....

     ....

(d) The manager of WeDriveAnyWhere would like the program to calculate the mean time for each journey in a variable named meanTime and then store the number of journeys, the total time and the mean time in a text file named DrivingData when the driver has finished his shift.

   Add the pseudo-code needed to do this.   **(3)**

   ....

   ....

   ....

   ....

(Total for Question 3 = 15 marks)

4   At the end of the year, WeDriveAnyWhere pay a bonus to their drivers. For full-time drivers this depends on the number of years they have worked for the firm and £100 is paid for each full year of service up to a maximum of £500.

For part-time drivers it depends on the number of hours worked in the year over 100 hours. The bonus is then £50 for every 100 hours worked up to a total of £300.

Complete the flowchart to show the process of determining the bonus for a driver.   **(6)**

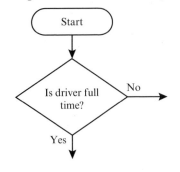

(Total for Question 4 = 6 marks)

5 Every year the firm has an annual dinner where an award is presented to the 'driver of the year'. The winner is the driver who has driven the greatest number of miles.

Here is a pseudo-code algorithm that identifies the 'driver of the year'.

1	`SET drivers TO ['Smith', 'Hamid', 'Cooper', 'Grantham', 'Parry']`
2	`SET miles TO [10000, 15000, 12000, 20000, 17000]`
3	`SET mileage TO 0`
4	`FOR count FROM 0 TO LENGTH(mileage) - 1 DO`
5	`  IF miles[count] > mileage THEN`
6	`    mileage = miles[count]`
7	`    SET position TO count`
8	`  END IF`
9	`END FOR`
10	`SEND 'The winner is ' & drivers[position] & ' with a mileage of ' & miles[position] TO DISPLAY`

(a) The driver and mileage data have been stored in arrays.

   (i) Describe **two** benefits of storing the data in arrays rather than using separate variables. **(4)**

   Benefit 1 ....

   ....

   ....

   Benefit 2 ....

   ....

   ....

   (ii) Explain why **two** 1-dimensional arrays have been used rather than **one** 2-dimensional array. **(2)**

   ....

   ....

   ....

   ....

(b) Explain why, in line 5, the loop runs from 0 to LENGTH(mileage) – 1 rather than to LENGTH(mileage). **(2)**

   ....

   ....

   ....

   ....

(c) Complete the trace table to show the execution of the pseudo-code.

You may not need to fill in all of the rows of the table. **(6)**

count	miles[count]	mileage	position	drivers[position]	Mileage[position]

(Total for Question 5 = 14 marks)

6 WeDriveAnyWhere store data about trips made by contract customers in database tables. Data about the trips is stored in one table and details about the contract customers are stored in another.

tbl_TRIP
Trip_Id
Date
Distance

tbl_CUSTOMER
Customer_Id
Address
Contact_Number
Contact_Name

(a) (i) Complete the diagram by adding a field from tbl_CUSTOMER to tbl_TRIP to form a relationship between the two tables. **(1)**

(ii) Explain why the relationship between the two tables is called a one-to-many relationship. **(2)**

....

....

....

....

(b) The firm would also like to be able to link driver details to the trips.

• Add a suitable table to the diagram containing three fields.

• Link the tables.

• Show the relationship between them. **(5)**

(Total for Question 6 = 8 marks)

7　When the drivers start work each day they must enter details into a computer program.

They must enter

- Their Driver_Id, which is in a standard format consisting of the first three letters of their surname, their initial and a digit between 1 and 9.

- The number of the taxi that they are using. The firm has 20 taxis.

These entries are validated and the text **ERROR** is displayed on the screen if they fail.

Part of the program is shown in the table below.

1	`SEND 'Please enter your driverID' TO DISPLAY`
2	`RECEIVE Driver_Id FROM (STRING) KEYBOARD`
3	
4	
5	
6	`SEND 'Please enter the taxi number.' TO DISPLAY`
7	`RECEIVE taxiNumber (INTEGER) FROM KEYBOARD`
8	
9	
10	

Complete the table by entering the missing lines required to validate the two entries.　　**(6)**

(Total for Question 7 = 6 marks)

8 WeDriveAnywhere needs a program to calculate the price of each trip according to the following specification.

- There is a basic charge of £3 with additional charges of
  - ○ 50 pence per mile for trips over 3 miles.
  - ○ 20 pence per minute over 5 minutes.
- From 11 pm and up to 6 am the total charges are doubled.
- Customers with a contract are given a 25 per cent discount. When users take out a contract they are given codes which are stored in a text file named Codes.txt. The driver must check that the code given by the user is valid.

Write an algorithm to meet the requirements.

Use pseudo-code or a programming language with which you are familiar.   **(11)**

....

....

....

....

....

....

....

....

....

....

....

....

....

....

....

....

....

....

(Total for Question 8 = 11 marks)

Answers

1. Algorithms

1 (a) An algorithm is a step-by-step procedure for solving problems.

(b) 1 selection; 2 iteration; 3 selection; 4 sequence; 5 selection; 6 sequence; 7 iteration; 8 selection; 9 iteration; 10 selection

(c) Two of: pseudo-code, flowcharts, draft program code

2. Algorithms: pseudo-code

1 (a) Pseudo-code is similar to a high-level programming language, but does not require exact syntax/indentation to be used. The programmer can concentrate on getting the logic of the program correct before turning it into executable code.

(b)
```
SEND 'Please enter a binary number.' TO
DISPLAY
RECEIVE binaryNumber FROM (STRING) KEYBOARD
SET placeValues TO [128, 64, 32, 16, 8, 4,
2, 1]      #An array stores the place values
of the digits
SET denaryNumber TO 0
#The digits will now be multiplied by their
place values
FOR index FROM 0 TO LENGTH(binaryNumber) - 1
DO
    SET denaryNumber TO denaryNumber +
    (binaryNumber(index) * placeValues[index])
END FOR
SEND denaryNumber TO DISPLAY
```

3. Algorithms: flowcharts

1 (a)

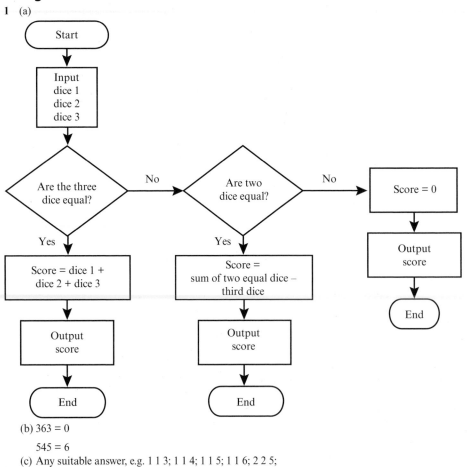

(b) 363 = 0

545 = 6

(c) Any suitable answer, e.g. 1 1 3; 1 1 4; 1 1 5; 1 1 6; 2 2 5; 2 2 6

4. Purpose of an algorithm

1 (a) To create login names for the students of a school.

(b) Their first name, family name, intake year and tutor group.

(c) 'check' is used to count the number of times the loop is executed.

(d) 01CooperRRed1

(e) Four from:

Intake year = 2002

Family name = Grantham

First name begins with the letter O.

Tutor group = Blue

There are two other students with a similar login name.

5. Completing algorithms

1 A: Is number2 > number3?

B: Is number1 > number3?

C: Output 'number2 is the largest'

6. Interpreting correct output

1

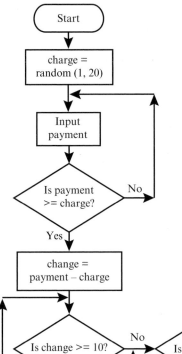
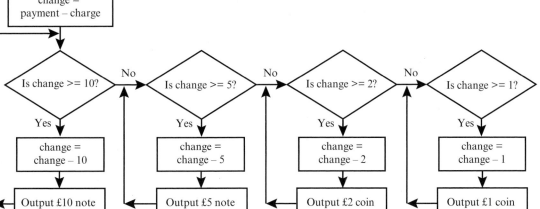

7. Using trace tables

1 (a) an array

(b) (i) line 4

(ii) `FOR search FROM 0 TO LENGTH(list) - 1 DO`

(c)

item	found	search	list[search]	output
13	False	0	5	
13	False	1	9	
13	False	2	2	
13	False	3	5	
13	True	4	13	
13	True	4	13	'The item is in the list.'

8. Identifying and correcting errors

1

1	Line 1	`SET charge to RANDOM(50)`
2	Line 10	`SET payment TO payment + money`
3	Line 13	`SEND 'Thank you. Change required is £' & change TO DISPLAY`
4	Line 18	`WHILE change >= 5.00 DO`
5	Line 24	`SET change TO change - 2.00`

9. Linear search

1 (a) A linear search algorithm starts at the beginning of a list and moves through item by item until it finds the matching item or reaches the end of the list.

(b)
```
SET found TO False
SET index TO 0
WHILE found = False AND index <=
LENGTH(partyList) - 1 DO
IF partyList[index] = "Elaine" THEN
    SET found TO True
END IF
SET index TO index + 1
END WHILE
IF found = True THEN
    SEND 'Elaine is on the list.' TO DISPLAY
ELSE
    SEND 'Elaine is not on the list.' TO
    DISPLAY
END IF
```

10. Binary search

1 Select the middle item (the median).
Compare this value with your search criterion. If they are equal, then stop.
If your search criterion is lower, repeat with the left-hand side of the list.
If it is higher, repeat with the right-hand side of the list.
Repeat these steps until the search criterion is found or there are no more items in the list to search.

2 Ahmed Ann Claire David Mary Matt Peter Stephen Zoe
Select the median item – Mary
Compare 'Stephen' with 'Mary'
New sub-list is Matt, Peter, Stephen, Zoe
Compare 'Stephen' with 'Peter'
New sub-list is Stephen, Zoe
Compare 'Stephen' with 'Stephen' – search item found

3 Compare 9 with 28
New sub-list is 1, 6, 9, 13, 15, 21
Compare 9 with 9 – search item found

11. Comparing linear and binary searches

1

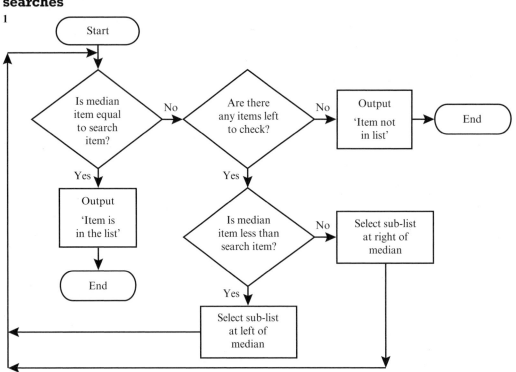

2 (a) 1..........**50**..........**100** first median is 50
    1..........**25**..........**49** second median is 25
    1..........**12**..........**24** third median is 12
    1..........**6**..........**11** fourth median is 6
    1..........**3**..........**5** fifth median is 3
    1..........**1**..........**2** sixth median is 1
There is only one number left (2) to select and therefore the maximum number of selections is 7.

(b) For a binary search, the data must first be sorted into ascending order. Sorting the data will take time so, for a small number of search items, a linear search might find the search item more quickly.
A linear search would be more efficient than a binary search if the item being searched for is the first item in the list.

12. Bubble sort

1

	20	15	3	13	9	2	6
Pass 1	15	3	13	9	2	6	20
Pass 2	3	13	9	2	6	15	20
Pass 3	3	9	2	6	13	15	20
Pass 4	3	2	6	9	13	15	20
Pass 5	2	3	6	9	13	15	20

2

1	SET swapped to True
11	END FOR
4	FOR index FROM 1 to LENGTH(list) − 1 DO
3	SET swapped to False
5	IF list[index − 1] > list[index] THEN
9	SET swapped TO True
10	END IF
6	SET temp TO list[index] − 1
2	WHILE swapped = True
7	SET list[index - 1] TO list[index]
12	END WHILE
8	SET list[index] TO temp

Marks for Bubble sort question 2 will be awarded for the following:

- 1 mark for getting the start and end of the 'while' loop in the correct positions
- 1 mark for getting the lines of the 'swap' in the correct order
- 1 mark for getting the start and end of the 'if' statement in the correct positions
- 1 mark for setting the value of 'swapped' correctly
- 5 marks for getting all lines correct.

13. Merge sort

1 Each small 'sub-problem' is easier to solve than one large problem.
It is more efficient to combine the solutions than to try to solve the main problem without using any techniques.

2

33	25	46	2	8	69	9

| 33 | 25 | 46 | 2 | | 8 | 69 | 9 |

| 33 | 25 | | 46 | 2 | | 8 | 69 | | 9 |

| 33 | | 25 | | 46 | | 2 | | 8 | | 69 | | 9 |

| 25 | 33 | | 2 | 46 | | 8 | 69 | | 9 |

| 2 | 25 | 33 | 46 | | 8 | 9 | 69 |

| 2 | 8 | 9 | 25 | 33 | 46 | 69 |

14. Decomposition and abstraction

1 (a) Abstraction means removing unnecessary detail to focus on the important elements.

(b) 'computerTurn' is an abstraction because it is a model or simulation of a real-life activity. The programmer doesn't need to know how the subprogram works – only that it returns an appropriate value.

(c) One possible algorithm is shown below. All solutions should compare the computer and player choices and decide who is the winner.

```
FUNCTION gameWinner(computerChoice, playerChoice)
#The choices of the computer and player are passed
to the function
BEGIN FUNCTION
#A check is first made to see if the game is a draw.
   IF playerChoice = computerChoice THEN
   SET result TO 'Draw'
#Now all the possible combinations are checked
      ELSE
         IF  playerChoice = 'R' AND computerChoice
         = 'S' THEN
            SET result TO 'Player wins'
      ELSE
         IF playerChoice = 'R' AND computerChoice =
         'P' THEN
            SET result TO 'Player loses'
      ELSE
         IF playerChoice = 'S' AND computerChoice =
         'R' THEN
            SET result TO 'Player loses'
      ELSE
         IF playerChoice = 'S' AND computerChoice
         = 'P THEN
            SET result TO 'Player wins'
      ELSE
         IF playerChoice = 'P' AND computerChoice
         = 'R THEN
            SET result TO 'Player wins'
      ELSE
         IF playerChoice = 'P' AND computerChoice
         = 'S THEN
            SET result TO 'Player loses'
      END IF
RETURN result    #The result is returned to the
main program
END FUNCTION
```

15. Variables and constants

1 (a) A variable is a container which is used to store values which can change as the program is running.

(b) The value stored in a variable can change during program execution, whereas the value of a constant always stays the same.

(c) They should be given meaningful names so that anyone reading the code will be given an indication of the types of value they are intended to contain, e.g. 'studentAge' rather than just 'X'.

(d)

Variable	Use within the program
mysteryNumber	This is used to hold the number which must be guessed.
correct	This is a 'flag' used to indicate whether the search item is in the list when it changes to True.
guess	This is used so that the user can enter a number.

16. Arithmetic operators

1 result = 6 * 8 / 2 + (15 − 6) + 3^3 (Brackets)
result = 6 * 8 / 2 + 9 + 3^3 (Indices)
result = 6 * 8/2 + 9 + 9 (Division)
result = 6 * 4 + 9 + 9 (Multiplication)
result = 24 + 9 + 9 (Addition)
result = 42

2

Code	Resultnumber
number = 12 + 6 / 2	15
number = 6 * 3 / 2	9
number = 23 MOD 6	5
number = 23 DIV 6	3
number = 6 ^ 2	36

3
```
SEND 'Please enter a number.' TO DISPLAY
RECEIVE  number FROM (STRING) KEYBOARD
SET result TO number * 2
SET result TO result + 6
SET result TO result / 2
SET result TO result – number
SEND result TO DISPLAY
```

17. Relational operators

1

Statement	True/False
7 * 3 <> 10 + 11	False
8 + 10 > 8 * 2	True
9 * 3 <= 10 + 17	True
10 + 15 >= 6 * 5	False
9 * 2 = 6 * 3	True

2
```
SEND 'Please enter the new mark.' TO DISPLAY
RECEIVE newMark FROM (INTEGER) KEYBOARD
SET equal TO 0
SET less TO 0
SET greater TO 0
FOR index FROM 0 TO LENGTH(marks) – 1 DO
   IF marks[index] = newMark THEN
      SET equal TO equal +1
   ELSE IF marks[index] < newMark THEN
      SET less TO less + 1
   ELSE
      SET greater TO greater + 1
   END IF
NEXT FOR
SEND 'Equal = ' & equal & 'Less = ' & less &
'Greater = ' & greater TO DISPLAY
```

18. Logical operators

1

Algorithm	Output

`SET number TO 3`
`IF number > 0 AND number < 2 THEN`
`   SEND 'Within range.' TO DISPLAY`
`ELSE`
`   SEND 'Out of range.' TO DISPLAY`
`END IF`
	Out of range

`SET number TO 6`
`IF NOT(number = 3) OR number <> 5 THEN`
`   SEND 'Number is acceptable.' TO DISPLAY`
`ELSE`
`   SEND 'Number is not acceptable.' TO DISPLAY`
`END IF`
	Number is acceptable

`SET colour TO 'red'`
`SET size TO 'm'`
`SET price to 25`
`IF colour = 'blue' OR colour = 'red' AND size = 'm' AND price <= 30 THEN`
`   SEND 'This would be OK.' TO DISPLAY`
`ELSE`
`   SEND 'Not OK.' TO DISPLAY`
`END IF`
	This would be OK

`SET number1 TO 6`
`SET number2 TO 9`
`IF (number1 <= 9 OR number2 >=10) AND NOT(number1 * number2 <50) AND (number2 – number1 = 3) THEN`
`   SEND 'These numbers are OK.' TO DISPLAY`
`ELSE`
`   SEND 'Not OK.' TO DISPLAY`
`END IF`
	These numbers are OK

19. Selection

```
1  SEND 'Please enter a mark between 0 and 100.'
   TO DISPLAY
   RECEIVE result FROM (INTEGER) KEYBOARD
   IF result >= 90 THEN
      SEND 'Excellent' TO DISPLAY
   ELSE IF result >= 70 AND result <= 89 THEN
      SEND 'Very good' TO DISPLAY
   ELSE IF result >= 60 AND result <= 69 THEN
      SEND 'Good' TO DISPLAY
   ELSE IF result >= 50 AND result <= 59 THEN
      SEND 'Satisfactory' TO DISPLAY
   ELSE
      SEND 'Unsatisfactory' TO DISPLAY
   END IF
```

20. Iteration

```
1  SET list TO [5, 9, 2, 5, 13]
   SEND 'Please enter the search item.' TO DISPLAY
   RECEIVE item FROM (INTEGER) KEYBOARD
   SET found TO False
   SET search TO 0
   WHILE found = False AND search <= LENGTH(item)
   - 1 DO
      IF item = list[search] THEN
         SET found TO True
      END IF
      SET search TO search + 1
   END WHILE
   IF found = True THEN
      SEND 'The item is in the list.' TO DISPLAY
   ELSE
      SEND 'The item is not in the list.' TO
      DISPLAY
   END IF
```

21. Data types

1 (a)

Data type	Variable
Real	meanHoursWorked
Boolean	fullWeek
Integer	day, oneDay, hoursWorked, daysWorked
Character	gender, name

(b) Variables will be needed for the pay per hour and the pay for the week.
Variable 1: payPerHour
Data type: Real
Variable 2: payForWeek
Data type: Real

22. String manipulation

1

Variable	Value
LENGTH(subject)	16
position	8

```
2  SEND 'Please enter a sentence in lower case.'
   TO DISPLAY
   RECEIVE sentence FROM (STRING) KEYBOARD
   SET a TO 0
   SET e TO 0
   SET i TO 0
   SET o TO 0
   SET u TO 0
   FOR index FROM 0 TO LENGTH(sentence) - 1 DO
      IF sentence(index) = 'a' THEN
         SET a TO a + 1
      ELSE IF sentence(index) = 'e' THEN
         SET e TO e + 1
      ELSE IF sentence(index) = 'i' THEN
         SET i TO i + 1
```

```
      ELSE IF sentence(index) = 'o' THEN
         SET o TO o + 1
      ELSE IF sentence(index) = 'u' THEN
         SET u TO u + 1
      END IF
   END FOR
   SEND 'a = ' & a & ' e = ' & e & ' i = ' & i & '
   o = ' & o & ' u = ' & u & '.' TO DISPLAY
```

23. Arrays

1 (a) An array is a data structure that can store multiple items of data, called elements, which are all of the same data type.

```
   (b) SET max TO 0
       SET min TO temp[0]
       FOR index FROM 0 to LENGTH(temp) - 1 DO
          IF temp[index] > max THEN
             SET max TO temp[index]
          END IF
          IF temp[index] < min THEN
             SET min TO temp[index]
          END IF
       END FOR
       SEND 'Maximum = ' & max & ' and minimum = ' &
       min TO DISPLAY
```

2

	0	1	2	3
0	0	1	1	0
1	1	0	0	1
2	1	1	1	1
3	1	0	0	1

24. File handling operations

```
1  (a) FOR index FROM 0 TO LENGTH(pixels) - 1
          WRITE shape.txt(pixels(index))
       END FOR
   (b) FOR row FROM 0 to 3 #A loop is set up for the
       4 rows of the matrix.
          FOR index FROM 0 to 3 #A nested loop is set
          up for the 4 items in each row
             SET matrix[row, index] TO READ shape.txt
             Record #The saved data is read into each
             item
          END FOR
       END FOR
```

25. Records

1 (a) Both arrays and records can store multiple data items in one structure. In arrays, the elements must be of the same data type but there can be elements of different data types in the same record.

(b) (i) A record would be better as different data types can be stored in the same record.

(ii) In a two-dimensional array the 'Weight' and 'Number of days' data would have to be stored as strings rather than real or integer data types.

(iii) An array could be used for the string data – Name, Gender and Special diet?.
Another array could be used for the integer data – Number of days.
Another array could be used for the real data – Weight(kg).
The items within each array would have to be in the same order.

26. Subprograms 1

1 (a) A subprogram is a self-contained sequence of program instructions that performs a specific task and is called whenever it is needed to carry out that task.

(b) 1 They make programs shorter. The code only needs to be written once and can be called as many times as needed.
2 They make testing easier as each section of code only has to be tested once even though it is used many times.

(c) A function returns data to the main program but a procedure does not.

2 (a) measurement

(b) newMeasurement

(c) RETURN newMeasurement

27. Subprograms 2

1 (a) Any two from: recLength, recWidth, recArea, recCircumference

(b) length, width

(c) area, circumference

(d) SET recArea, recCircumference TO calculate(recLength, recWidth)

2
```
FUNCTION findLargest(one, two)
BEGIN FUNCTION
    IF one > two THEN
        SET largest TO one
    ELSE
        SET largest TO two
    RETURN largest
END FUNCTION
#Main program
SEND 'Please enter the first number.' TO DISPLAY
RECEIVE numberOne FROM (INTEGER) KEYBOARD
SEND 'Please enter the second number.' TO
DISPLAY
RECEIVE numberTwo FROM (INTEGER) KEYBOARD
SET largestNumber TO findlargest(numberOne,
numberTwo)
SEND largestNumber TO DISPLAY
```

28. Validation

1
```
SET validated TO False
WHILE validated = False DO
    SET validated TO True
    SEND 'Please enter a password.' TO DISPLAY
    RECEIVE password FROM (STRING) KEYBOARD
    WHILE password = '' DO
        SEND 'You have not made an entry.' TO
        DISPLAY
        SEND 'Please enter a password.' TO DISPLAY
        RECEIVE password FROM (STRING) KEYBOARD
    END WHILE
    IF LENGTH(password) < 8 THEN
        SEND 'Password is less than 8 characters
        in length.' TO DISPLAY
        SET validated TO False
    END IF
    SET numberUpper TO 0
    FOR index FROM 0 to LENGTH(password) - 1
        IF password(index) >= 'A' AND
        password(index)) <= 'Z' THEN
            SET numberUpper TO numberUpper + 1
        END IF
    END FOR
    IF numberUpper = 0 THEN
        SEND 'No upper case letters.' TO DISPLAY
        SET validated TO False
    END IF
END WHILE
SEND 'Password OK.' TO DISPLAY
```

29. Testing and test plans

1 (a)

Test number	Type of test	Test data	Expected result
1	Normal data test	69	Data will be accepted
2	Boundary data test	99	Data will be accepted
3	Erroneous data test	120	Data will not be accepted and an error message will be shown

(b)

Line number	Correct version
2	FOR index FROM 0 TO LENGTH(students) - 1
9	SET marks[index] TO percentage
10	IF percentage > maximum THEN

30. Using binary

1 The processor which executes the program instructions consist of billions of transistors.

Each transistor has two states – either it transmits an electric current (it is on) or it doesn't (it is off).

The binary system has two digits – 1 and 0.

Digit 1 can represent the on state and digit 0 the off state.

2 C

3 000, 001, 010, 011, 100, 101, 110, 111

4

1	0	1	1
8	0	2	1

5 The answer is the *context* in which the computer uses the binary code and the program instructions it is following. If it sends the code to a speaker, sound is produced. If it sends the code to a monitor, a pixel on the monitor will be populated with the colour of that code, etc.

31. Converting from denary to binary

1

Comparison	Binary digit	Remainder
199 > 128	1	71
71 > 64	1	7
7 < 32	0	7
7 < 16	0	7
7 < 8	0	7
7 > 4	1	3
3 > 2	1	1
1 = 1	1	0

11000111

2
```
SEND 'Please enter the denary number.' TO
DISPLAY
RECEIVE denary FROM (INTEGER) KEYBOARD
SET binary TO ''
SET placeValues TO [128, 64, 32, 16, 8, 4, 2,
1]
FOR index FROM 0 to LENGTH(placeValues) - 1 DO
    IF placeValues[index] >= denary THEN
        SET binary TO binary & '1'
        SET denary TO denary - placeValues[index]
    ELSE
        binary = binary & '0'
    END IF
END FOR
SEND binary TO DISPLAY
```

32. Converting from binary to denary and binary addition

1

Binary	1	0	0	1	0	1	1	1
Place values	128	64	32	16	8	4	2	1
Decimal	128	0	0	16	0	4	2	1

The answer can be calculated using a table like the one shown here. However, you don't need to use a table, but you must show the additions of the separate place values:

Decimal = 128 + 16 + 4 + 2 + 1 = 151

2
```
  0 1 0 1 0 1 1 1
  0 1 0 1 1 1 1 1
 ¹1 0 ¹1 ¹1 ¹0 ¹1 ¹1 0
```

3 (a)

```
    1 1 0 0 1 0 1 1
    1 0 0 1 0 1 1 1
  ─────────────────
  1 0 1 ₁1 ₁0 ₁0 ₁0 ₁1 0
```

(b) (i) overflow error

(ii) The result produces a number that is greater than can be represented by 8 bits, so 9 bits are required. In denary, the number is greater than 255.

4 Incorrect

```
  0 1 0 1 0 1 1 1
  0 1 0 0 1 0 1 0
  ─────────────────
  ₁1 0 ₁1 ₁0 ₁0 ₁0 0 1
```

33. Logical shifts

1 (a) A binary shift is used when a binary number is being multiplied or divided by powers of 2. Shifts to the left are used for multiplication. Shifts to the right are used for division. A 1 place shift multiplies or divides by 2^1 (2). A 2 place shift multiplies or divides by 2^2 (4).

(b) 10101100

2 (a) The binary number would be divided by 4.

(b)

Binary number	10101101	Denary equivalent	173
Binary number after a 2 place logical right shift	00101011	Denary equivalent	43

(c) In a 2 place logical right shift, the binary number is being divided by 4. The expected answer would be 43.2 but there is a loss of precision as the result in binary is given to the nearest lower integer (whole number) because the answer does not have decimal places.

34. Signed integers

1 (a) The leftmost bit, which is known as the most significant bit (MSB), is used to indicate whether a number is positive (0) or negative (1). The MSB is the sign, and the rest of the bits indicate the size or magnitude of the number.

(b) Zero can be either positive or negative OR Additions do not always give the correct result.

2

24	0	0	0	1	1	0	0	0
Two's complement	1	1	1	0	1	0	0	0

3 (a)

30	0	0	0	1	1	1	1	0
−15	1	1	1	1	0	0	0	1
Answer	0	0	0	0	1	1	1	1

(b)

Answer	0	0	0	0	1	1	1	1
Place values	128	64	32	16	8	4	2	1

Denary equivalent is 15.

4

−10	1	1	1	1	0	1	1	0
−20	1	1	1	0	1	1	0	0
Answer	1	1	1	0	0	0	1	0

35. Arithmetic shifts

1 (a) When carrying out an arithmetic shift right to an 8-bit signed binary number, the bits are shifted to the right but are replaced at the left by copies of the most significant bit. The result is that the number is divided by the number of shifts.

(b) When carrying out an arithmetic shift left to an 8-bit signed binary number, the most significant bit is left in place and the other bits are shifted left. The places at the right are replaced with 0s. The result is that the number is multiplied by the number of shifts.

2

Number	1	0	0	1	0	1	0	1
Result of shift	1	1	1	1	0	0	1	0

3

Number	1	0	0	1	0	1	0	1
Result of shift	1	1	0	1	0	1	0	0

4

35	0	0	1	0	0	0	1	1
−35	1	1	0	1	1	1	0	1
Result of multiplication	1	1	1	1	0	1	0	0

36. Hexadecimal and binary

1 (a) Hexadecimal is used because people get confused with large binary numbers. Binary numbers can be simplified by writing them in hexadecimal notation, which means that fewer numbers are needed.

(b) C3 is equal to the denary numbers 12 and 3.
12 and 3 represent the two nibbles of the binary number. Therefore the binary number = 1100 and 0011 = 11000011.

(c) (i) 11010101 = the two nibbles 1101 and 0101.
These are equal to the two denary numbers 13 and 5. Therefore the hexadecimal number = D5.

(ii) 10111101 = 1011 and 1101 = 11 and 13 = BD.

37. Characters

1 (a) The character set is the list of binary codes that can be recognised by the computer hardware and software.

(b) ASCII is a 7-bit code. There are 128 code sequences representing English characters and control actions such as SPACE and SHIFT. The codes are grouped according to function, e.g. codes 65 to 90 represent the upper case letters of the alphabet.

2
```
SET codes TO ''
SEND 'Please enter a sentence.' TO DISPLAY
RECEIVE sentence FROM (STRING) KEYBOARD
FOR index FROM 0 TO LENGTH(sentence) - 1 DO
    SET codes TO codes + ASC(sentence(index))
    IF index = < LENGTH(string) THEN
        SET codes TO codes &' '  #This will add a
        space unless it is the last character in
        the string.
    END IF
END FOR
```

38. Bitmap images

1 (a) The size of an image is given as the number of pixels in its width (W) and height (H).
The resolution of an image is the number of pixels per unit area of the display.

(b)

Colour depth	Number of colours represented
1	2
3	8
8	256

(c) File size = W × H × colour depth = 2000 × 3000 × 24
= 2000 × 3000 × 24 / 8 / 1024 / 1024

39. Sound

1 (a) The sampling frequency describes the number of sound samples that are taken each second.

(b) Increasing the sampling frequency gives a more accurate reproduction of the analogue wave, as more samples are taken with less time between them.

2 (a) The bit depth describes the number of bits used to encode the data taken in each sample.

(b) A high bit depth allows more data to be stored and allows the dynamic range of the sound to be more accurately represented.

3 Length of recording and number of channels (e.g. mono or stereo).

4 File size (bits) = sample frequency × bit depth × recording length = 100 × 44100 × 16 / 8 / 1024 / 1024

40. Units

1 (a) binary
  (b) Processing is carried out by billions of transistors which operate in one of two states, on and off, equivalent to 1 and 0.

2

byte	megabyte	terabyte	bit	kilobyte	gigabyte	nibble
3	5	7	1	4	6	2

3 72 000 000 000 / 8 / 1024 / 1024
4 20 × 1024 × 1024 × 1024 × 1024 × 8

41. Data compression

1 (a) Any two of the following.
  • It uses less internet bandwidth when they are sent and received.
  • The transfer speed is quicker.
  • The files take up less storage space on their computers.
  (b) Lossless compression reduces file sizes without deleting any data. When the file is decompressed, it is exactly the same as the original. Nothing is lost. Lossless compression looks for redundancy, where the same data is stored many times, and groups this data into one reference in the file.
  Lossy compression reduces the file size by deleting some data. The original can never be reconstituted when it is decompressed as it has been irreversibly changed.
  (c) PDF file: lossless.
  The novel would be impossible to read if some of the data (words) were removed permanently.
  Images of her trip to London: lossy.
  Areas with very similar colours are merged into one to reduce file size. People cannot distinguish these small differences and so are not aware that the data has been removed.

42. Run-length encoding

1 (a) Data redundancy in a data file is where the same item of data is repeated many times, e.g. in a text file each letter is repeated many times.
  (b) Run-length encoding would be more suitable for a black and white image as there are only two items of data and there will be runs of the same item of data. In a full-colour image there are millions of different items of data and so there will be fewer, if any, runs of the same data.

2 (a)

Encode data	Compressed using run-length encoding
bbbbbb	6b
bwwwwb	1b4w1b
bwwwwb	1b4w1b
bbbbbb	6b
bwwwwb	1b4w1b
bwwwwb	1b4w1b

  (b) before 36 bytes; after 28 bytes

43. Encryption

1 (a) Encryption is the encoding/scrambling of data into a form that cannot be understood by unauthorised recipients.
  (b) When data is transmitted between authorised users it can be intercepted and also when it is stored it can be accessed by unauthorised personnel. The data should therefore be converted into a form that they cannot understand.

2

Plain text	Key	Cipher text
The battle is won	+ 3 or right 3	wkh edwwoh lv zrq
Send more troops	– 3 or left 3	Pbka jlob qollmp

3

Plain text	Key	Cipher text
Gzzgiq ot znk iktzxk	+ 6 or right 6	Attack in the centre
Yofkd x elopb	– 3 or left 3	Bring a horse

44. Structured and unstructured data

1 (a) Structured data is data that is stored in an organised way according to similarities and differences between the data.
  Unstructured data is not stored in any organised way. As new data is acquired it is just added without trying to fit it in with existing data.
  (b) When data is structured, links can be made between the items of information so that it can be searched to create information and reports.

2 D
3 books, students, borrowing
4

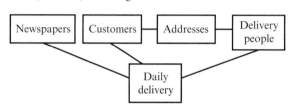

45. Attributes and tables

1 A
2 Any suitable, such as Title, Author, Publisher, ISBN, Length, Genre
3 (a) **A** is record and **B** is field
  (b) A primary field is a field which holds unique data or information in each record. It is needed by the database software to be able to identify each record.
  (c) None of the fields will hold unique data, e.g. there could be many of the same make, with the same colour, using the same fuel etc.
  The designers could add a field to store unique information, e.g. 'Registration Number' or give each record its own unique number in the table such as 'Car Number'.

46. Relational databases

1 A relational database allows data elements in one table to be related to any piece of data in another table, as long as both tables contain a common element.
2 C
3 (a) Any two of: easier to sort, search, produce reports, analyse data, keep the data organised.
  (b) (i) primary key
      (ii) foreign key
      (iii) One of: to form relationships (links) between the tables; to allow queries across the tables; to relate the records in one table with the records in another.
  (c) 0 to 255

47. Input–processing–output

1

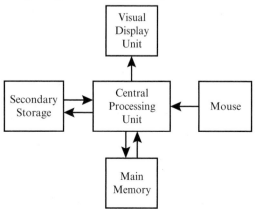

2   The computer performs a series of actions on the input data according to the instructions in the program it is following. This is done by the CPU (central processing unit) in the processor.

3

Device	Stage
Keyboard	Input
Microphone	Input
Printer	Output
Central processing unit	Processing
Speakers	Output
Monitor	Output

48. The central processing unit

1

Internal hardware components	Function
CU (control unit)	Controls the other components of the CPU.
Clock	Controls the rate at which program instructions are carried out.
ALU (arithmetic logic unit)	Performs arithmetic and logical operations to carry out program instructions.
Cache	Stores frequently used program instructions and data so the processor isn't kept waiting for them to be transferred from the main memory.
Registers	Memory locations. Some perform special functions in the fetch–decode–execute cycle.

2   A laptop with a 3 GHz CPU could have a better performance as it has a higher clock speed. This means that it will process program instructions more quickly than a computer with a 2 GHz processor, so programs will run faster.
However, the 2 GHz computer could have more cache memory to store frequently used instructions. It could also have a greater number of cores, which improve performance by allowing multitasking and parallel processing.
The 2 GHz computer could also have more RAM, which would improve performance because the CPU would not have to use virtual memory.

49. Components of the CPU

1   The Von Neumann model describes the way in which the CPU is designed and carries out instructions with other components. It is an architecture in which both the data and instructions are stored in memory.

2   Any two from:
• memory to store program data and instructions
• program counter
• input and output devices (could include secondary storage devices, keyboard mouse, printer, loudspeaker etc.).

3   The CU coordinates the actions of the computer. It sends out control signals to other parts of the CPU and to other components of the computer.
The ALU performs arithmetic and logical operations. It carries out activities such as:
• addition, subtraction, multiplication and division
• comparisons between two different numbers.

4   Registers are memory locations within the CPU where data is stored so that it can be accessed very quickly. Some of these perform special functions, e.g. storing the memory address for the next instruction, but others are general purpose.

5   The decoder works out what the program instructions mean or the actions that they require the CPU to carry out.

50. Fetch–decode–execute cycle

1   Any two from:
• control bus; during the fetch cycle, the control unit sends a 'read' signal to the RAM along the control bus
• address bus; the control unit uses the address bus to send signals specifying the required memory location in the RAM
• data bus; contents of a memory location are transferred to the CPU along the data bus.

2   (a)

Description	Order
The next instruction is sent from the RAM to the CPU.	2
The instruction is carried out.	4
The CU interprets the instruction.	3
The CPU sends a signal to the RAM requesting the next instruction.	1

(b) RAM is where the program instructions and data are stored until they are needed.

(c)
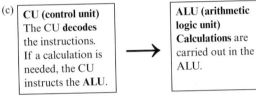

CU (control unit)
The CU **decodes** the instructions. If a calculation is needed, the CU instructs the **ALU**.

ALU (arithmetic logic unit)
Calculations are carried out in the ALU.

51. Memory

1   (a) Volatile memory provides temporary storage for program instructions and data. It loses its content when the electrical power is switched off.

(b) Non-volatile main memory is used for instructions that do not need to be changed in normal use. For example, the sets of instructions needed for a computer to start are stored in ROM.

2

Statement	True
RAM stands for Random Access Memory	✓
ROM is volatile	
Data can be read from and written to ROM	
Program instructions and data are stored in RAM	✓
The sets of instructions needed for a computer to start are stored in ROM	✓

3   RAM is volatile but ROM is non-volatile.
RAM can be written to and read from, but ROM can only be read from.
RAM stores program instructions and data, but ROM is used to store the sets of instructions needed for a computer to start.

4   One from: Sets of instructions needed for the computer to start; Data used by a program when it is executing.

52. Magnetic and optical storage

1   (a) Two reasons which could include:
• Data that is stored in RAM is lost when the power is turned off because RAM is volatile.
• A secondary storage device, such as a hard drive, provides permanent storage for data that would otherwise be lost when the power is turned off.
• Data can be moved between computers using secondary storage devices.

(b) (i) Magnetic storage devices use electromagnets in their read/write heads to read and write the data, which is encoded as opposing magnetic polarities on the surface of the disk or tape.

(ii) Optical disks use a laser to read and write data. The data is encoded as a series of pits in a spiral track running from the inside to the outside of the disk.

(c) Data can be written to and read from magnetic devices far more rapidly than from optical devices. This improves the performance of the data processing.

2 200 photos at 8 MB each needs a total of 200 × 8 MB = 1600 MB = 1.6 GB.
A single CD can store 700 MB, so Noah's photos cannot be saved on a single CD.
A single DVD can store 4.7 GB, so his photos can be saved on a single DVD.

53. Solid-state memory

1 Solid-state drives consist of flash memory.
Flash memory consists of transistors that keep their charge even when the power is switched off.
At first, all transistors are charged (set to 1) but when a save operation begins, current is blocked to some transistors, switching them to 0.

2 (a) It is called a solid-state storage device because it has no moving parts.
(b) solid-state drives; USB drives

3 magnetic, optical, solid state

4 Any two from: lighter and more portable; no moving parts that can be damaged if dropped; data access speeds are faster than for magnetic storage.

54. Cloud storage

1 (a) Cloud storage is off-site storage made available to users over a network, usually the internet.
(b) In your exam, your answers to 6-mark questions will be marked on how well you present and organise your response, as well as content containing the relevant knowledge and concepts. Your responses should contain most or all of the points given in the answers below, but you should also make sure that you show how the points link to each other, and structure your response in a clear and logical way.
Answers could include the following points.

If data is stored in the 'cloud' then users will need an internet connection to access them.
Users will not need an internet connection if they are stored locally.

If data is stored in the 'cloud' then users can access the data from anywhere in the world.
If data is stored locally then users can access it only on site.

If data is stored in the 'cloud' then access times are affected by the speed of an internet connection.
If data is stored locally access speeds are not affected by the internet connection.

Employees of the organisation will be responsible for backing up and restoring data if it is stored locally.
The 'cloud' storage provider will be responsible for backing up and restoring data.

The organisation will be responsible for buying, maintaining and upgrading devices for storing the data if it is stored locally.
The 'cloud' storage provider will be responsible for this.

The organisation will be responsible for the security of the data if it is stored locally.
The 'cloud' storage provider will be responsible for this.

When working collaboratively, files can be synced automatically between users when it is stored in the 'cloud' wherever they are in the world.
This cannot be done if it is stored locally.

55. Embedded systems

1 (a) An embedded system is a computer system built into another device in order to control it.
(b) For example: processor, memory, input and output interfaces.

(c) Examples of devices that have embedded systems include: washing machine, microwave oven, television, camera.

2 (a) Desktop computers are designed to run a range of different applications, such as word processors, spreadsheets, DVD players, games, while each embedded system is designed to perform a small, specific range of functions linked to the device it is embedded into.
(b) Embedded systems are described as real-time systems because they must guarantee a response almost immediately in order for the system to react to different situations.
(c) Assembly language is used so that the hardware can be directly controlled by the programs written. This is far more efficient than using a high-level language that needs an interpreter or compiler.

56. Logic

1 (a)

INPUT		OUTPUT
0	0	0
0	1	1
1	0	1
1	1	1

(b)

INPUT	OUTPUT
0	1
1	0

2

A	B	P
0	0	0
0	1	0
1	0	1
1	1	0

3

A	B	C	P
0	0	0	1
0	0	1	0
0	1	0	0
0	1	1	0
1	0	0	0
1	0	1	0
1	1	0	0
1	1	1	0

57. Logic circuits

1 (a) (A OR B) AND NOT (C)
(b)

A	B	C	P
0	0	0	0
0	0	1	0
0	1	0	1
0	1	1	0
1	0	0	1
1	0	1	0
1	1	0	1
1	1	1	0

2 (a) NOT(A) AND NOT(B)
(b)

A	B	P
0	0	1
0	1	0
1	0	0
1	1	0

58. Operating system 1

1 Systems software's role is to control the operation of the computer hardware, allow software to run, provide an interface for computer users, maintain the computer system and manage user interactions with the computer system.

2 (a) The operating system checks that memory requests are valid, allocates memory to processes when needed and frees up memory for other uses when no longer needed. It also swaps out data to the virtual memory when the main memory is full.

(b) File management is used to create a folder and file structure for data. This makes it easier for users to organise and find data in a systematic way.

(c) File permissions control who can create a file, who can see or open a file, who can write to a file or edit it and who can delete a file.

59. Operating system 2

1 (a) The operating system:
   - requires a login name for each individual user of a computer.
   - requires each user to provide a password for security
   - creates folders in which users can store their work.
   When a user installs software, the operating system allows them to install it just for themselves or for all users.

(b) The user interface:
   - allows the user to communicate with the computer
   - translates user input by the keyboard or mouse into a form that the computer hardware and software can understand and execute.
   Many operating systems provide a graphical user interface (GUI) while others allow the user to type in commands. These are called command line interfaces.

2 Peripherals are controlled by the operating system using programs called drivers. The drivers carry out the necessary translations to allow the CPU and the devices to communicate correctly.

60. Utility software 1

1 (a) Data is fragmented when parts of files are saved to different parts of the hard disk.

(b) Defragmentation software reorganises files which have been split across different parts of the disk by putting pieces of related data back together. Fewer disk accesses are then needed to read the data. This improves performance and can free up more space on the hard disk.

(c) (i) When he is attaching a file to an email or uploading it to a website.

(ii) Lossless compression reduces the file size without discarding any of the data and the original file is restored when it is decompressed.
Lossy compression reduces the file size by discarding some of the data, so the original file cannot be restored when it is decompressed.

(d) (i) incremental backup

(ii) Not all of the files are backed up each time – only the ones that have been added to or changed since the last backup.

2 Encryption software is used to scramble data into a form that cannot be used by unauthorised users. This protects the data from unauthorised use.

61. Utility software 2

1 B

2 (a) Virus – it enters the computer system hidden within another program.
It can corrupt or delete data on a disk.

(b) Spyware – it comes packaged with other software, such as free software.
It spies on users by sending screenshots and key presses to the hacker's computer, so revealing details of passwords.

3 One type scans for viruses using a database of known virus definitions (also called signatures) which should be kept up to date. They identify viruses by comparing them to the signatures.
Another type uses a set of rules to detect viruses by looking at their behaviour, such as a program which tries to copy itself into another program or a program which tries to remain resident in memory after it has finished executing.

4 C

62. Simulation and modelling

1 (a) A computer model attempts to abstract the rules and mechanisms that control real-life systems and apply them in computer programs so that they can be used to simulate the behaviour of those systems under different conditions.

(b) Any two suitable examples such as a flight simulator, weather forecasting, traffic flow.
NOT financial models.

(c) Any **two** from:
Safety – ability to experiment without harming people or the environment.
Financial – new products can be tested without having to build prototypes, e.g. cars and aeroplanes.
Repetition – tests can be quickly repeated to ensure similar outcomes.
Adjustments – changes to the rules and input data can be made quickly to see the outcomes.

(d) Any two from:
The mathematical calculations may be too complex to model 'real-life' situations.
It may be difficult to identify all of the rules correctly.
The model is not reality so the answers might not be correct; reality might turn out differently.
The processing power needed to run the model may be greater than what is available.

63. Programming languages

1 (a) Assembly language

(b) Machine language or machine code

(c) Language 1 is a high-level language as it is very similar to a human language. It has to be translated before it can be processed by the CPU. Language 2 is a low-level language as it is very similar to machine code and each command represents a similar command in language 3. Language 3 is a low-level language because it can be directly processed by the CPU.
You could also answer by saying that languages 2 and 3 are at a low level of abstraction while language 1 is at a high level of abstraction.

(d) (i) 1 High-level programs are less time-consuming to write and also to test as the language is similar to a human language.
2 High-level programs are portable from one machine to another as they are independent of the CPU.

(ii) 1 Programs written in low-level languages require less memory and execution time.
2 Low-level languages allow the programmer to directly control system hardware and are used extensively for programming embedded systems.

64. Translators

1 (a) an assembler

(b) A compiler translates the source code into a standalone, machine code program (object code) which can then be executed by the processor. An interpreter translates the high-level code line by line. It is needed each time the program is run.

(c) An advantage of a compiler is that the program is translated once only and as a separate process. When it is run, it is already translated into machine code so it is executed more rapidly. A disadvantage is that you cannot change the program without going back to the original source code, editing that source code and recompiling. An advantage of an interpreter is that when an error is found, the interpreter reports it and stops so the programmer knows where the error has occurred. A disadvantage is that every line has to be translated each time it is executed and it is therefore slower.

2 The set-top receiver must process data quickly and so a compiler is used because compiled code runs faster than interpreted code.

65. LANs and WANs

1 (a) A network is a group of computer systems and devices linked together so that they can communicate and share resources.
   (b) 1 The users can share resources such as printers and internet connections.
   2 Files can be shared by users across the network allowing users to work collaboratively.

2 (a)
   • A LAN is a network in a small area such as a home, school, office building or group of buildings on a single site.
   • A LAN is usually managed by a local manager or team at the site.
   • It is owned by the organisation that uses it.
   (b)
   • A WAN connects separate LANs over a large geographical area to form a network of networks. The internet is a WAN.
   • Computers in a WAN can communicate with computers and users in other locations.
   • A WAN is managed by several different people or parts of an organisation working together.

66. Client–server and peer-to-peer networks

1 (a)
   • In peer-to-peer networks, there is only one type of computer and there is no server to manage the network.
   • All the computers are equal and they can communicate with each other directly without having to go through a server.
   • Each user can give other users access to their computer and their programs and to any devices attached to them, such as printers.

   (b) Any two from:
   • Expensive server and network operating systems are not required, so it is cheaper.
   • Specialist staff are not required to administer and maintain the network, which saves money.
   • A peer-to-peer network is much easier and requires less specialist knowledge to set up.
   (c) 1 All data can be saved on the file server, so it can all be backed up at the same time without having to back up the data on each computer separately.
   2 Network security is stronger because access to file servers is controlled centrally using login names and passwords.

67. Wired and wireless connectivity

1 (a) Data is transmitted along copper cables as electric signals. In fibre optic cables, data are transmitted as pulses of light generated by a light emitting diode (LED) or a laser.
   (b) Advantage: Signals are transmitted over longer distances and at faster speeds.
   Disadvantage: It is more expensive than copper cable.

2 (a) Radio waves are used to transmit data across networks using frequencies of between 2.4 and 5 GHz.
   (b) Each frequency range is divided into separate channels. For example, in the 2.4 GHz range used by most networks, there are 14 channels spaced 5 MHz apart. Users can change the operating channel of their Wi-Fi device to prevent interference.

3 (a) Security is good in a cable network as each computer has to be physically plugged into the network using a cable. Security is poor in a wireless network as anyone within range could log into the network.
   (b) There is no interference in a cable network as the cables through which the data is transmitted can be shielded.
   In a wireless network, signals can be affected by other electronic equipment and obstacles such as walls.
   (c) In a cable network bandwidth is high – up to 10 Gbps. In a wireless network bandwidth is lower – up to 600 Mbps.

68. Connecting computers to a LAN

1 (a) A NIC provides a physical connection to either a wired or a wireless network for a device on the network. The NIC formats the data so that it can be transmitted and received across the network.
   (b) Every NIC is created with its own unique media access control (MAC) number programmed into it. Because all devices on the same network have different MAC addresses it enables the senders and recipients of data to be uniquely identified.

2 A switch transmits the data to the intended recipient only, whereas a hub broadcasts it to all the devices on the network. Sending the data to only the expected recipient reduces the network traffic and improves the efficiency of the network.

3 (a) A wireless access point enables wireless devices to connect to cabled networks.
   (b) The router connects two networks – the home network and the internet link provided by the family's internet service provider.
   The router sends the requests from each of the home computers to internet servers and distributes the incoming data to the correct computers as identified by their IP addresses.

69. Data transmission

1 (a) So that a high bandwidth isn't needed for large files.
   (b) Component 1: header
   Function: contains the source and destination addresses and the position of the packet in the complete message.
   Component 1: body
   Function: contains some of the data.
   Component 1: footer
   Function: to inform the receiving device that this is the end of the packet.

2

Name of layer	Purpose	One protocol in the layer
Application layer	Provides services to applications such as web browsers and email clients.	HTTP
Transport layer	Divides data sent from application layer into packets. Checks that data sent has been received and notifies sender that data has been received.	TCP or UDP
Internet layer	Adds the source and destination. IP addresses to the data and routes it to the recipient computer.	IP
Network access layer	Uses network-specific protocols to ensure correct transmission of data through the local network.	Ethernet

70. Protocols

1 (a) Protocols are used to control:
- data formats, to ensure that data can be exchanged consistently and accurately
- address formats, to identify senders and recipients and to ensure that data goes to the right addresses
- routing, to provide the right information so that data can flow through networks correctly.

(b)

Protocol	Function
HTTPS	Used when communications between a client and host have to be encrypted.
SMTP	Provides the rules for sending email messages from client to server and then from server to server until they reach their destination.
HTTP	Provides the rules to be followed by web browsers when accessing websites and by web servers when requesting and supplying information.
FTP	Provides the rules for transferring files between computers.

(c) (i) transmission control protocol/internet protocol

(ii) TCP divides data sent from the application layer into packets. It checks that data has been sent correctly and has been received, or notifies the sender that data has not been received.

IP adds the source and destination IP addresses to the data and routes it to the recipient computer.

71. Network topologies 1

1 (a)

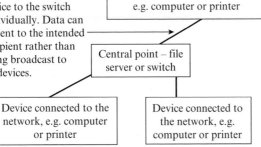

Cable connecting each device to the switch individually. Data can be sent to the intended recipient rather than being broadcast to all devices.

Device connected to the network, e.g. computer or printer

Central point – file server or switch

Device connected to the network, e.g. computer or printer

Device connected to the network, e.g. computer or printer

(b) Three reasons could include:
1 Data is sent directly to only the intended computer and therefore network traffic is kept to a minimum.
2 If one link fails, all the other devices will continue to operate, as data is sent to each computer individually.
3 It is easy to add new devices without disrupting the network, as each device has its own communications cable.

72. Network topologies 2

1 (a) Diagrams similar to the following.

(b) (i) A data collision is where data packets collide with each other because two or more devices have transmitted packets at the same time.

(ii) There are no data collisions on a ring network because all data travels in one direction from node to node until it reaches its destination.

Devices can only use a token if it is empty.

2

Network topology	Characteristic
Star	Each device is connected to a central switch.
Bus	Each device is connected to a central cable with a T-piece.
Mesh	Each device has a dedicated connection to all other devices on the network.
Ring	Nodes cooperate to take turns sending data.

73. Network security 1

1 Your answer could include some of the following ideas.
- Network security protects the data stored by organisations and ensures that only authorised users can access the network and its resources.
- It ensures that users can only access files relevant to themselves and not others to which they are not authorised. This prevents misuse such as deleting information and copying and removing data.
- The safe storage of personal data such as names, addresses and health and financial information is important as it is a legal requirement to ensure its security under The Data Protection Act.
- Data stored on the network is important to the functioning of an organisation and if it is stolen, deleted or corrupted then the organisation may fail.
- The loss of data may have financial implications as it may contain details of new products or marketing campaigns which would be of value to competitors.
- All organisations rely on the programs and data stored on their networks; without it they are not able to function as they usually do not have any paper-based copies.

2 (a) Any three from:
- Use strong passwords of at least 8 characters including non-alphanumeric characters, such as ! or ?
- Regularly change the password.
- Never reuse old passwords.
Do not use personal information, e.g. date of birth or other memorable dates, children's names etc.
- Never write down a password.
- Use different passwords for each secure environment.

(b) Access control is used to set a network user's rights to the files and data stored. This ensures that confidential data is seen only by the required users. This means that files cannot be viewed, edited, modified or deleted by unauthorised users.

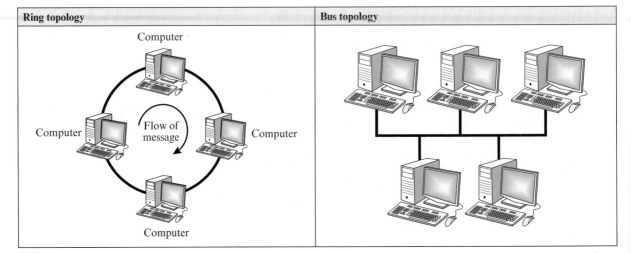

Ring topology	Bus topology

Ring topology: Computer, Computer, Flow of message, Computer, Computer

74. Network security 2

1 (a) Any three from:
   - Keep access doors locked and fit them with security recognition measures, for example keypads or biometric systems such as fingerprint pads or iris scanners to prevent unauthorised access.
   - Use swipe cards containing users' details to authenticate users entering the building.
   - Install closed-circuit television to monitor the exterior and interior of the building.
   - Install burglar alarms and monitors in all rooms to warn if anyone is accessing an area that should be empty.
   - Fit radio frequency identification (RFID) chips to all equipment so that an alarm will sound if the equipment is taken out of the building.
   - Use chains and locks to attach equipment to work benches to prevent equipment from being removed from the building.

   (b) Firewalls are either software or hardware devices that protect against unauthorised access to a network, and are primarily used to prevent unauthorised access from the internet.
   They can be configured to prevent communications from entering the network and also to prevent programs and users from accessing the internet from the network.
   A firewall can inspect the incoming packets and reject those that are from IP address not on a trusted list or block communication to certain external IP addresses.

75. Cyberattacks

1 Your answer could include two of the following techniques.
   - Phishing is when fraudsters send emails claiming to be from an actual organisation such as a bank or e-commerce site in order to find out personal and financial details.
   - The emails usually have false links where the recipients are asked to click on a link which leads to a website controlled by the criminals.
   - 'Shoulder-surfing' involves finding login names, passwords, credit card and PIN (personal information numbers) details by direct observation, e.g. by someone in an office watching others entering passwords or an employee at a shop or petrol station watching a PIN being entered. Binoculars or closed-circuit television can be used to watch from a distance or record users entering sensitive information.

2 (a) eavesdropping or 'data interception and theft'
   (b) Criminals use programs called packet analysers or 'packet sniffers' to intercept the packets travelling on a network, which are then analysed and their data are decoded. The criminals can therefore steal sensitive data such as logins, passwords, credit card numbers and PINs.
   (c) The organisation should encrypt all data on the network.

3 - Smart devices in homes have IP addresses and can be connected to home networks and the internet.
   - Most people do not bother to change the administrator password and hackers can take charge of the devices and use them for distributed denial of service attacks where they flood websites with login requests and cause them to crash.

76. Identifying vulnerabilities

1 (a) Your answer could include three of the following.
   - What users can and cannot do on the network.
   - When backups will be made and where they will be kept.
   - When and who is responsible for applying software patches and operating system updates.
   - What should be done if there is a problem or breach of security.
   - Any other suitable response.

   (b) Penetration testing is the testing of a computer system, network or web application to find vulnerabilities that an attacker could exploit. The test then indicates how those vulnerabilities could be exploited to demonstrate the havoc that could be caused. The test finds vulnerabilities in computer systems and networks that an attacker could exploit and tests the effectiveness of network security policies.

   (c) These software tools are also called 'vulnerability scanners' and assess computers, computer systems, networks or applications for known security weaknesses that have already been identified in other systems or software. They must therefore be updated as new weaknesses are identified.

   (d) Ethical hacking is carried out by a computer and networking expert who systematically attempts to penetrate a computer system or network without written permission, or on behalf of its owners, for the purpose of finding security vulnerabilities that a malicious hacker could potentially exploit. They then notify the owner of the system about these security flaws.

77. Protecting software systems

1 Your answer could include three of the following security issues.
   - Whether the software will be exposed to hackers.
   - If authentication is required.
   - Whether access control is required.
   - What warnings will be given to users if they try to delete information.
   - Whether data will need to be encrypted.

2 **Code reviews** look at security vulnerabilities in the code. Reviews can be carried out by other programmers (or teams of programmers) or automated reviews by specialist software which highlights potential security vulnerabilities.
   Modular testing – a module is an independent block of code that implements a small number of routines. As only a small amount of data is being tested, any security issues can be easier to identify and fix.

3 An audit trail provides a record of all network activity. It allows a technician to study which user has accessed programs and data, when they accessed them and what they did. It also shows what has happened during a cyberattack.

4 As security issues are identified in operating systems, software patches are produced to rectify them. Most users rarely search for these updates and install them. It is therefore better to have them automatically applied without the user having to be proactive.

78. The internet

1 (a) Ayana will need to use the infrastructure – the backbone and cables – of the internet for which there is a charge. ISPs pay the organisations who create and maintain this infrastructure and then charge individual users like Ayana for their use. The ISP also provides Ayana with an IP address.

   (b) (i) This is a unique software address to identify Ayana's computer. When she requests pages and communicates with websites they use this address to which to send the data.

   (ii) For version 4 addresses (IPv4), IP addresses consist of 4, 8-bit numbers separated by full stops, e.g. 192.168. 169.13. This is 32 bits in total. Version IPv6, which is being introduced, uses 128 binary bits to create the address, so that more are available for devices.

2 (a) When data is transmitted, it is split into segments which are incorporated into packets. Each packet consists of a header, containing the destination and source IP addresses, a body containing the data and a footer to inform the receiving device that it has reached the end of the packet successfully.

(b) The packets of data are transmitted using a technique called packet switching whereby they are sent by different routes depending on the state of the internet – a part of the internet may not be functioning or there may be congestion.

Routers have routing tables which are essentially lists of rules stating where to send packets for different destinations. When a router receives a packet it looks in the packet header for the destination address and then uses the rules within the routing table to decide where to send it. A packet will need to be forwarded between several routers before it reaches its destination.

79. The world wide web

1 (a) The WWW is a network of online content which is hosted on servers throughout the internet.
      The content is made up of web pages which are linked together by hypertext links.
    (b) HTML is a markup language. The scripting language typically used is javascript.
    (c) HTTP or HyperText Transfer Protocol
    (d) The URL is a textual representation of the protocol to be used and the IP address and is easier to remember and enter than 32 binary numbers or their denary equivalent. The part of the URL containing the IP address is called the domain name.
    (e) When Lianne enters the URL her computer sends a request to a server of the Domain Name Service to resolve the domain name back into its IP address.
      If the server does not have that domain name in its database, it sends a request to another DNS server and so on until the IP address is returned to the first server. The IP address is returned to Lianne's computer which then uses the IP address to contact the website.

80. Environmental issues

1 Your answer could include some of the following ideas.
   Energy
   • Manufacture and use of devices uses energy. Manufacturing involves energy-intensive mining and processing of minerals. The use of devices involves the energy used by the devices themselves, but also by data centres. These data centres generate heat, so energy is needed to keep them cool.
   • Much of the energy used comes from non-renewable sources such as gas and coal.
   • Computer science is used in efficient energy production. Computer software is used to design, model and test efficient devices to produce electricity from wind, wave and solar power.
   • Energy use can be reduced using smart technologies, such as light-sensitive switches that turn off lights when they are not needed.
   • Efficient transport planning using computer modelling and analysis can reduce fuel use.
   Sustainability
   • Digital devices use many different chemical elements. Some of these are rare and will be in short supply as they are used up. It is difficult to recycle devices to reuse these elements.
   Waste
   • Electronic devices are difficult to recycle and are often disposed of in landfill sites as e-waste.
   • Landfill sites take up areas of land that could be used for other purposes.
   • Toxic substances such as lead, mercury and cobalt can get into the soil and the water supply from the landfill sites and cause health problems.
   Data analysis
   • Computer science technology can be used to monitor environmental factors by transmitting and analysing data. This data can be shared by scientists around the world who can collaborate to find solutions to problems.
   • Computers can be used to develop models to forecast environmental behaviour and identify options for action.

81. Ethical impact

1 (a) Ethical behaviour means acting in ways that are considered good or moral by society.
    (b) (i) The 'digital divide' describes the gap between the digital 'haves' and 'have-nots'; between those who can access digital technology and those who cannot.
      (ii) Your answer could include some of the following ideas.
        • The digital divide can be caused by many factors, such as a lack of access to broadband, being unable to afford to access it or having very low IT literacy.
        • It can have many negative impacts such as poor employment prospects by having low IT literacy.
        • A lack of access means that households without internet access have to pay far more as they cannot shop or pay bills online.
        • A lack of access can lead to social isolation, as people with no access to the internet are less likely to keep in touch with family and friends.
        • On a national level, economic growth is poor in countries with poor access to technology as they cannot compete with countries that do have access.
        • Technology also makes for a more inclusive society for people who are able to access it. For example, people can access online education, adaptive technologies allow people with disabilities to participate more fully in society. The technology links people with common interests wherever they are in the world promoting a feeling of belonging.

2 She could prioritise the requests in the following ways:
   • Response 3 would be the most ethical as she is considering which would be the most harmful and she is not taking into consideration how much she will be paid.
   • Response 1 is less ethical as she is not acting in a professional way as she is not fully using her knowledge and experience to the benefit of her clients.
   • Response 2 would be the least ethical as she is considering her payment over the needs of all of her customers.

82. Privacy issues

1 Your answer could include some of the following ideas.
   • Technology allows companies and government organisations to find out details of people's activities and to track their movements.
   • Surveillance cameras are commonplace in most towns and cities in Britain. With the advent of number plate recognition, it has been claimed that a person can be tracked on a journey through London in a car and on foot. Britain has more surveillance cameras per head of population than any other country in Europe.
   • Many people have complained that being tracked, filmed and photographed without their permission is an infringement of their privacy.
   • Mobile phone use allows people's movements to be tracked as they move to different cells or mobile phone masts. This can be considered as an infringement of one's privacy.
   • Internet service providers and companies, such as Google, record every search carried out and website visited. This can be used to find out what users are interested in and target advertisements directly at them. This can be considered as an infringement of privacy, especially if the companies hand over this information to the government authorities.
   • Surveillance cameras help prevent antisocial behaviour. If criminals know they are being filmed, they will not attack people and property. Criminal acts can also be stopped if they are seen on surveillance cameras. Videos from surveillance cameras can be used as evidence in criminal prosecutions.
   • Surveillance cameras can help to find missing people. Some people say that people shouldn't be worried if they are not doing anything wrong but others argue that it is dangerous for governments to be able to know exactly what you are doing and where you are.

- Tracking a person using their mobile phone can help to solve crimes and verify that criminals were in a particular area.
- People's search history can be used to find out what users are interested in and target advertisements directly at them.
- The analysis of huge amounts of personal data can lead to better-informed decision making and planning such as improvements in public health and smarter cities geared to the movements of their inhabitants.

83. Legislation

1 (a) All original work, including images, music, documents and videos.
   (b) The person who creates the work owns the copyright.
   (c) For example:
      1 The person could be sent to prison.
      2 The person could be prevented from using the internet by their internet service provider.
2 For example:
   1 So that others can include their work and include it within their own with or without attribution depending on the type of licence.
   2 So that others can modify and build upon their work and redistribute it.
3

Action	Type of offence
A student accesses another student's email account without permission.	A
A user accesses parents' stored credit card numbers and security codes in order to buy goods online fraudulently.	C
A student guesses the login names and passwords of other students and logs into their accounts.	A
A student gains access to class results and changes their own marks and grades.	B
As a challenge, a student manages to guess the password of one of the administrative staff to gain entry to the management system.	A

84. Proprietary and open-source software

1 (a) Proprietary software is commercially produced by an organisation for a profit.
   (b) Any one from:
      - Software is developed professionally and carefully tested.
      - Support will be provided to keep customers happy so that they will continue to use the software.
      - There will be books, magazine articles and online tutorials.
      - Updates and bug fixes meet the needs and suggestions of the users.
   (c) Any one from:
      - Users can study the source code to see how the software works.
      - Users can change and upgrade the software.
      - It is free to use.
      - There is a community of dedicated enthusiasts who will provide help and support.

2

Statement	Proprietary	Open-source
The source code cannot be modified by anyone but the person, team, or organisation that created it.	✓	
It is free to use.		✓
Users can modify the source code to adapt it to their needs and can pass it on to other users free of charge.		✓
The software must be paid for.	✓	
Users can study the source code to see how the software works.		✓
It may need specialist knowledge to install the software.		✓
The support and updates may be expensive.	✓	
The software will be developed carefully and tested thoroughly because people will be paying money to use it and they will be cross if it doesn't work.	✓	
There is a community of dedicated enthusiasts who will provide help and support.		✓

Practice Paper 1

Principles of computer science

1 (a)

Component	Function
CU (control unit)	The CU controls the other components of the CPU and coordinates the fetch–decode–execute.
Address bus	The address bus carries memory addresses from the CPU and the memory to uniquely identify the memory address to be used.
Clock	The clock emits a pulse at regular intervals to synchronise the actions of other parts of the CPU.
Registers	Registers are storage locations inside the CPU used to hold an instruction, an address or other single item of data.
ALU (arithmetic logic unit)	The ALU performs arithmetic and logical operations to carry out program instructions.
Data bus	The data bus carries the item of data to be read from or written to memory to or from the CPU.

(b)

	RAM	ROM
Program instructions and data are stored here.	✓	
It is used to boot up the laptop when it is switched on.		✓
It is volatile.	✓	

(c) Frequently used instructions are stored in the cache which contains memory which is faster than that used in the RAM. These instructions can therefore be 'fetched' more quickly and improve performance.

(d) C

2 (a)

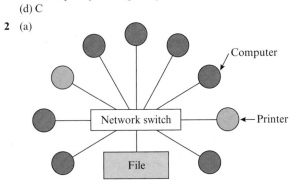

Network switch

Computer

Printer

File

(b) Two of the following but each point should be developed.
- The server is responsible for network security by allocating login names and passwords to users.
- The server can allocate the access rights of the users so that different users can read, edit or delete different files.
- The server stores all of the programs and files for the users so that they can be accessed from any of the workstations.
- The server can centrally back up all data that is stored so that each client workstation does not have to be backed up independently.

(c) (i) A protocol is a set of rules for formatting data that is sent over a network so that it can be understood by the sending and receiving computers.
(ii) D

(d) Answer to include items listed in the specification for this – access control, physical security and firewalls.
- Authentication is the process of determining whether someone trying to log into the network is who they claim to be. This is commonly accomplished by giving all users a login name and password. The organisation should have a policy for the use of passwords, e.g. it should be strong – at least eight characters and include non-alphanumeric characters such as ! or ? It should also be changed regularly, never written down or shared and old passwords should never be reused. Multifactor authentication involves two or more pieces of information, e.g. knowledge of a password plus a biometric identification or knowledge of a secret fact such as the first school attended.
- Physical security is often the first line of defence to prevent unauthorised people from entering the buildings where the network equipment is located. Precautions should include keeping access doors locked and fitting them with security recognition measures, such as keypads or biometric systems (e.g. fingerprint pads, iris scanners). Swipe cards containing users' details for entry to the building should be issued and closed circuit television to monitor the exterior and interior of the building should be installed.
- A firewall protects a network connected to a WAN such as the internet. Firewalls can be software or hardware based and are used to prevent access from computers with unknown IP addresses. They can also prevent employees accessing undesirable websites.

3 (a) (i)
- Instructions in high-level code use words whereas in machine code instructions are in binary code.
- High level code can be portable/translated for different machines whereas machine code is specific to a particular machine.
- High-level code is designed to be read by human programmers whereas machine code is to be read and executed by the computer.

(ii)
- The program can be written more quickly as the programmers are using a language more like their own natural language.
- There will be fewer errors in the code as the programmers are using a familiar language.
- The programmers will not have to write completely new code for each device the game is to be played on.

(b) (i) Translates one line of code at a time and executes it. It stops when it finds an error and can be resumed.
(ii) compiler

4 (a) The CPU of a computer which executes program instructions contains billions of transistors acting as switches.
They are either on or off. They have only two states: they either transmit an electric current or they do not.
As there are only two states (off or on), they can be represented by the two digits of the binary system: 0 and 1.

(b) (i) 100100101 (1 mark for each 4 digits)
(ii) Overflow error.

(c) 128 + 32 + 16 + 8 + 2 + 1 = 187

(d) (i) F7
(ii) There are 4 bits for each hexadecimal digit and so it is easy to convert.
There are less digits and so easier to remember and enter.

5 (a) (i) pixels
(ii) The colour depth states the number of bits used to represent the colour value of each pixel.
(iii) Either: 4288 × 2482 × 24 / (8 × 1024 × 1024)
Or: 4288 × 2482 × 24 / 8 / 1024 / 1024

(b) (i) The file size is reduced by removing some of the information and so when the file is decompressed it is not the same as the original.
(ii) Areas with very similar colours are merged into one to reduce file size. People cannot distinguish these small differences and so do not realise the data has been removed. If data is removed from text files there will be missing letters and it may become unintelligible.

6 (a) An array allows multiple items of data to be stored under one identifier or name.

(b)

Laos	Cambodia	India	Australia	Nepal	Peru
Cambodia	India	Australia	Laos	Nepal	Peru
Cambodia	Australia	India	Laos	Nepal	Peru
Australia	Cambodia	India	Laos	Nepal	Peru

(c) India, Nepal, Peru

7 (a) P = (A AND B) OR C

A	B	C	P
0	0	0	0
0	0	1	1
0	1	0	0
0	1	1	1
1	0	0	0
1	0	1	1
1	1	0	1
1	1	1	1

(b) (i) (A AND B) AND NOT(N)

(ii)

A	B	N	L
0	0	0	0
0	0	1	0
0	1	0	0
0	1	1	0
1	0	0	0
1	0	1	0
1	1	0	1
1	1	1	0

Practice Paper 2

Application of computational thinking

1 (a) Any suitable such as car, driver, time, distance, cost.

(b) cost = 3 + (miles × 0.5) + (minutes × 0.2)

(c)

Input	Process	Output
Time for each journey	Sum times for each journey	Total time driven
Total money taken during the day	Total money taken / Number of journeys	Mean charge per journey
Number of drivers on duty	Number of trips / Number of drivers on duty	Mean number of journeys per driver

2 (a) 800

(b) The variable 'yes' on line 2 has not been initialised before the start of the loop.
The following line should be inserted between lines 1 and 2:
SET use to 'yes'

(c) (i) 5
The variable dayNumber has been written as dayNUMBER
(ii) syntax error

(d) (i) 60
(ii) The DIV operator returns an integer and only whole people are required.

(e) SEND 'The number of part-time drivers required is ' & partTime TO DISPLAY

(f) 10

3 (a)

Feature	Line number
Iteration	5
Comment	1, 12, 15, 16 or 19
Indentation	Any of 6 to 9 and 15 to 20

(b) (i)

Variable	Data type
numberJourneys	integer
tripTime	real
repeat	character

(ii) Global – one of: numberJourneys, journeyTime, totalTime, repeat
Local – one of: startTime, endTime, tripTime, reply

(c) (i) Any two of:
• allow the production of structured code
• make programs shorter – the code only needs to be written once and can be called as many times as needed
• make program code easier to read and test
• shorten the development time of a program
• make testing easier
• make code more readable.

(ii) Type of subprogram: Procedure
How it is different: Does not return a value to the main program

(d) SET meanTime TO totalTime/numberJourneys
WRITE DrivingData.txt numberJourneys, totalTime, meanTime

or

WRITE DrivingData.txt numberJourneys, totalTime, meanTime
Note that the variables must be in the correct order.

4

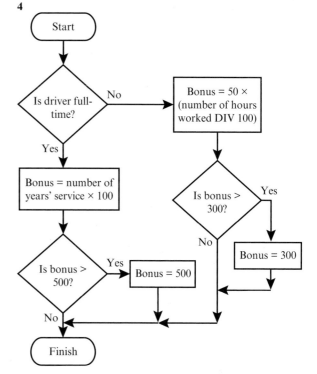

5 (a) (i) An array requires only one identifier (name) whereas variables would each require their own individual ones. An array requires only one loop whereas each variable would require separate ones.

(ii) All the data in an array must be of the same type and in this case both integer and string data types have been used. They cannot both be included in a 2-dimensional array.

(b) The index of the array starts at 0 and the last index will therefore be 1 less than the length of the array, e.g. if the length of the array is 4 then the indexes will be 0, 1, 2 and 3.

(c)

count	miles [count]	mileage	position	drivers [position]	Mileage [position]
		0			
0	10000	10000	0		
1	15000	15000	1		
2	12000	15000	1		
3	20000	20000	3		
4	17000	20000	3		
4	17000	20000	3	Grantham	20000

6 (a) (i) Customer_Id
(ii) It is called a one-to-many relationship because each customer appears only once in tbl_CUSTOMER but many times in tbl_TRIP.

(b)

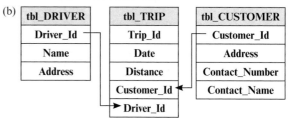

Any suitable fields and field names for the driver table.

7 3 IF LENGTH(Driver_Id) <>5 THEN
  4   SEND 'ERROR' TO DISPLAY
  5 END IF

  8 IF taxiNumber < 1 OR taxiNumber > 20 THEN
  9   SEND 'ERROR' TO DISPLAY
 10 END IF

(2 marks for each line involving operators, and 1 mark for each of lines 4,5 and 9,10, if both lines are correct.)

8 As this is an algorithm represented in pseudo-code or a programming language, there is no 'correct' solution. The 'ideal' is one that meets all of the requirements as accurately and efficiently as possible.

The following is a sample solution.

```
SEND 'Enter distance (miles)' TO DISPLAY
RECEIVE distance FROM (INTEGER) KEYBOARD
SEND 'Enter duration of trip (minutes)' TO
DISPLAY
RECEIVE duration FROM (INTEGER) KEYBOARD
IF distance > 3 THEN
    SET charge TO 3 + ((distance - 3) * 0.5)
ELSE
    SET charge to 3
END IF
IF duration > 5 THEN
    SET charge TO charge + ((duration - 5) *
    0.2))
END IF
SEND 'Please enter the hour as on a 24 hour
clock' TO DISPLAY
RECEIVE hour FROM (INTEGER) KEYBOARD
IF hour >= 23 OR hour <= 6 THEN
    SET charge TO charge * 2
END IF
SEND 'Does the user have a contract (y or n)?'
TO DISPLAY
RECEIVE contract FROM (CHARACTER) KEYBOARD
IF contract = 'y' THEN
    SEND 'Enter the customer's code.' TO DISPLAY
    RECEIVE code FROM (STRING) KEYBOARD
    SET found to False
    WHILE found = False DO
        FOR EACH Record FROM Codes.txt DO
                READ Codes.txt Record
            IF Record = code THEN
                SET found TO True
                SET charge to charge -
                (charge/100*25)
            END IF
        END FOREACH
    END WHILE
END IF
SEND 'The cost of the trip is ' & charge TO
DISPLAY
```

Notes

Notes

Notes

Published by Pearson Education Limited, 80 Strand, London, WC2R 0RL.

www.pearsonschoolsandfecolleges.co.uk

Copies of official specifications for all Pearson qualifications may be found on the website: qualifications.pearson.com

Text and illustrations © Pearson Education Ltd 2017
Typeset and illustrated by Tech-Set Ltd, Gateshead
Produced by Out of House Publishing
Cover illustration by Miriam Sturdee

The right of David Waller to be identified as author of this work has been asserted by him in accordance with the Copyright, Designs and Patents Act 1988.

First published 2017

20 19 18
10 9 8 7 6 5 4 3 2

British Library Cataloguing in Publication Data
A catalogue record for this book is available from the British Library

ISBN 978 1 292 13119 1

Printed in Slovakia by Neografia

Acknowledgements
The author and publisher would like to thank the following individuals and organisations for permission to reproduce photographs:

Photographs
Shutterstock.com /Iakov Kalinin 38; ifong/Shutterstock.com / ifong 85; Shutterstock.com/ Nick Hawkes 90.
All other images Pearson Education

Notes from the publisher
1. While the publishers have made every attempt to ensure that advice on the qualification and its assessment is accurate, the official specification and associated assessment guidance materials are the only authoritative source of information and should always be referred to for definitive guidance.

    Pearson examiners have not contributed to any sections in this resource relevant to examination papers for which they have responsibility.
2. Pearson has robust editorial processes, including answer and fact checks, to ensure the accuracy of the content in this publication, and every effort is made to ensure this publication is free of errors. We are, however, only human, and occasionally errors do occur. Pearson is not liable for any misunderstandings that arise as a result of errors in this publication, but it is our priority to ensure that the content is accurate. If you spot an error, please do contact us at resourcescorrections@pearson.com so we can make sure it is corrected.